HOW TO FEED YOUR DOG

HOW TO FEED YOUR DOG

Trevor Turner
B Vet Med, MRCVS

POPULAR DOGS
London Melbourne Sydney Auckland Johannesburg

Popular Dogs Publishing Company Ltd

An imprint of the Hutchinson Publishing Group

3 Fitzroy Square, London WIP 6JD

Hutchinson Group (Australia) Pty Ltd
30–32 Cremorne Street, Richmond South, Victoria 3121
PO Box 151, Broadway, New South Wales 2007

Hutchinson Group (NZ) Ltd
32–34 View Road, PO Box 40–086, Glenfield, Auckland 10

Hutchinson Group (SA) (Pty) Ltd
PO Box 337, Bergvlei 2012, South Africa

First published 1980
© Trevor Turner 1980

To Jean, without whose nimble fingers and typing expertise my enthusiasm, despite all the support and encouragement from without, would have waned far before the winning post was in sight.

Contents

Acknowledgements

Today no book can result from one person's work alone and therefore it is with grateful thanks I acknowledge all the support and help given to me in the preparation of this manuscript.

In particular I am grateful to the commercial food manufacturers who, on hearing of the project, unreservedly provided information concerning their products; my veterinary colleagues, to some of whom I applied for information rather like a hungry dog at a bone: thank you for your forbearance. To my working colleagues in the hospital who unselfishly tried to protect the boss from interruption while tackling the research and fighting with the mechanics of getting the words actually on to paper. To my publishers and Gerald Austin in particular who, with tact and patience, steered me along the path of first-time authorship. To my clients and patients, without whose help my experience would have been sadly lacking and who convinced me of the need to make the effort to record this experience. Lastly, but far from least, my long-suffering family and dogs. Compared with other professions and occupations, a practising veterinarian suffers a deficit of family life. To allow me to swallow up hour after hour of this precious free time in writing this book shows unparalleled tolerance and forbearance. Thank you all.

Illustrations

Author's Introduction

Despite all the strains on the economy in recent years, the popularity of the dog as a pet, particularly in urban and suburban situations, continues to grow. Everyone of us who acquires a dog has a daily repetitive task to perform – to feed our charge – how do we gain the knowledge to do this properly? If we are not very good at preparing meals for ourselves we can always seek advice from the myriad of publications on cookery and diet, but what can we do for our dogs? There is a dearth of publications on dog feeding and nutrition which is probably why I, and my colleagues in general practice, are consulted so frequently for advice on feeding and are confronted even more frequently by the errors in performing the task.

It was in the hope of filling this gap that this book was written, based on years of experience as owner, breeder and veterinary surgeon interested in dogs. I have tried to share my experience and at the same time introduce sufficient theory to allow you, the reader, to judge whether to embark on a home-prepared diet or to go 'commercial' and to ensure that if you choose the latter course, your final selection, amid the bewildering and ever-increasing variety, is made on rather more than the persuasiveness of a television advertisement. I have attempted to cover in a readable and not too indigestible manner the theory and the diets necessary for dogs in all situations, from the puppy to the elderly; the show dog to the urban pet; dogs in health and dogs with a variety of disease problems.

At the same time I wanted to avoid the image of a text or reference book but wished to present something that could be dipped into at will for the provision of immediate information. This has involved a certain amount of deliberate repetition, first to ensure that basic concepts of nutrition are understood, irrespective of the particular dietary problem for which the reader is seeking guidance, and secondly to ensure that this is achieved without having to rifle through the pages for the facts. The classic example of this is perhaps my preoccupation with fats as the natural energy source for the dog, supplied in the form of cooking oil.

Whether I have been successful in my objects only you, the reader, can judge.

I will be delighted to receive your comments and criticisms.

The composition of food: general principles and a bit of theory

There are at present something like $5\frac{1}{2}$ million dogs in the United Kingdom and those of us who own these animals must have some experience of feeding since this is a task we perform at least once every day of the year. How many of us, however, get it right? Judging by the number of obese animals that any veterinary surgeon in practice sees in the course of his daily work, one assumes that perhaps the majority of us get it only *too* right, *too* much of the time!

Obesity presents just as many problems as any other serious disease. For example, as the dog grows fatter, more strain is put upon the joints and the bones of the legs which are not designed to withstand this and in consequence the poor animal will frequently develop a chronic lameness which is irreversible, even if the weight is subsequently drastically reduced. Indeed, it is known scientifically that only 10 per cent obesity can result in these irreversible joint changes occurring.

The usual reaction when told that our pets are putting on weight is to endeavour to exercise them more, but again this can be fraught with danger, because if the animal is seriously obese, exercise will only create more stress on the joints and on the other vital body systems and consequently heart and chest diseases are not uncommon in the fat dog.

Where do we go wrong then? Obviously as dog owners the majority of us do go wrong since we very successfully feed our dogs and yet end up with dogs that are no longer healthy but are often fat, sluggish and not infrequently in pain. Is it that we feed the wrong things or just in too large quantities? In order to fully answer these questions and to understand our mistakes, it is worth while looking at the general principles of canine nutrition from the scientific viewpoint.

The number of foods that dogs find appetizing is very large and when these are compounded into diets, the range is almost limitless. However, it must be remembered that all foods contain basically the same six components, all of which are of some value to the animal.

(1) Water

(2) Inorganic elements and minerals known together as ash

(3) Fats

(4) Proteins

(5) Carbohydrates

(6) Crude fibre

The diagram shows how food is broken down scientifically into these components.

Thus food contains basically water and dry matter. The percentage of water varies from food to food. Cow's milk contains approximately 87 per cent; fresh lean meat or fish 70 per cent; cereal grains, wheat, peas etc. about 10 per cent. Even dry dog biscuits contain at least 8–10 per cent of water.

Dry matter contains:

(1) *Ash* which is the scientific name for those elements which are essential to the health and growth of the animal, for example, sodium, potassium, calcium, phosphorus etc.

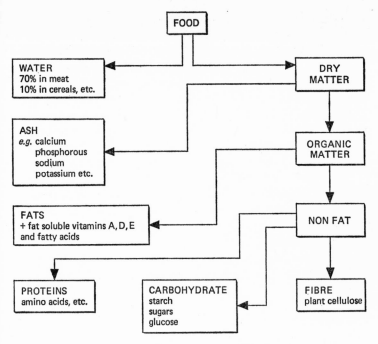

Figure 1 Six components of food

(2) *Organic matter* which is divided into fats and fat soluble vitamins A, D and E, and the non fatty part which is further sub-divided into:

(a) proteins
(b) carbohydrates
(c) crude fibre.

The dog is a meat eater or carnivore. Its teeth have adapted for tearing or cutting rather than grinding as in the case of ruminants such as the cow. It also has a relatively short and simple gut, designed to cope with the needs of enzymic digestion when compared with the long and complicated gut found in the vegetarian goat, sheep or cow, which has to deal with large quantities of fibre in the form of plant cellulose, the digestion of which depends upon bacterial action, which is much slower than the usual enzymic digestion that occurs in the dog.

Do not be misled however, into thinking that the dog is a meat eater and needs nothing else. Anyone keeping dogs will know that at times they will eat grass or other vegetable matter and will often do this with obvious enjoyment. Theories for this behaviour range from those who say the dog eats grass because it feels nauseated and does it in order to make itself sick, to those who say that it is an inborn need for more fibre as a bulking agent to ensure bowel regularity. I must admit that I would tend to subscribe to this latter theory.

Protein in the form of meat is in short supply in the world today but modern technology and knowledge of nutrition has in the last few years ensured that other sources of protein, which would normally be totally unpalatable to a dog, can be incorporated into diets and accepted with enthusiasm. Soya beans, for example, which no self-respecting dog would look at in their natural state have, as a result of modern processing methods, been converted into a highly palatable source of protein, incorporated into many commercial dog diets.

Provided we can ensure a healthy dog, I see no reason why such products should not be exploited.

What do we mean by health? We mean a dog that has a bright eye and a glossy coat, that has sound, straight limbs and is of the correct size and weight for its type and age. We also mean a dog that, when adult, retains the ability to produce a healthy litter as necessary. Such a definition of health could not be met if the dog was fed a diet lacking any of those six important components; therefore let us look at each one more closely.

(1) *Water* Over 70 per cent of the dog's body is composed of water and we all know what would happen if he was denied this essential ingredient of his diet for more than a few hours. He obtains his water by drinking and also by those digestive processes during which hydrogen oxidizes. In addition, some water is obtained from the water content in all foodstuffs.

It is lost from the animal via the urine and the faeces and also by evaporation, particularly from the lungs and tongue and also the feet and pads. Although water balance is a delicate mechanism, provided water is always readily available to the animal, he can manage without human aid. Specimens of the larger breeds, and also adult dogs can conserve far more water than those of the smaller breeds or puppies, which obviously require far more frequent drinks than, for example, an adult Wolfhound or St Bernard. I think this is also one of the reasons why small breeds are so much more prone to distress following car journeys in hot weather.

(2) *Minerals* There are many minerals found in the ash content of food that are known to be required by the dog and a mixed diet will ensure an adequate supply of the majority of these. However, it should be remembered that very few foods suitable for dog feeding contain more than about 30 per cent of ash or inorganic elements. Exceptions to this are, of course, bones and boneflour and the latter can be a very valuable addition to many diets, particularly since the phosphorus and calcium contained in high proportions are among the more important minerals required, particularly by the growing animal. Other

important minerals are iron, copper, potassium, sodium, and chlorine, combined together to form sodium chloride, or salt, and also magnesium.

(3) *Fats* Fats contain more energy per unit of weight than any other foodstuff and for the dog are its natural sources of energy. Dogs do not require, however, solely animal fat. Vegetable fats as incorporated for example in margarine and also found in many cereal grains are also useful. Vitamin E (alphatocopherol) so beloved by dog breeders, is found in large quantities in wheat germ and is virtually unknown in animal fats.

The other fat soluble vitamins A and D are essential for bone growth. They are found in greatest quantity in cod liver and halibut liver oil, although animal fats do contain appreciable quantities. Vitamin K, the other fat soluble vitamin, which is necessary for the clotting of the blood, is found naturally in such unlikely foods as spinach, egg yolk, hemp seed etc.

Fats are composed of fatty acids and glycerol. These are split during digestion and certain of the fatty acids, especially those known as unsaturated fatty acids, are especially important in certain skin diseases. These are found particularly in certain vegetable oils and it is for this reason that veterinary surgeons will prescribe margarine or rape oil for dogs suffering from certain types of eczema.

Fatty acids also play a part in the building of complicated compounds such as steroids and also phospholipids, which are important in nutrition in the dog. Do not confuse fatty acids with amino acids, which are the breakdown products of protein and are the main means by which protein products are transported by the bloodstream from one part of the body to another. The dog tends to store its energy in the form of fats which, when stored under the skin, act as a good insulator against heat and cold, helping the dog's coat in this respect. Diets containing around 10 per cent of fat are satisfactory for growth and maintenance of most dogs, although some animals need up to 20 per cent if their energy requirements are high, e.g. in the case of sled dogs.

Since fat can become rancid due to oxidization, most dried or semi-moist foods are low in fat content and abundant in carbohydrate.

(4) *Protein* Without protein the dog's life could be measured in weeks instead of years. Cereal grains contain about 10 per cent of protein, dried peas and beans around 20 per cent, while nuts are a rich source going up to possibly 25 per cent which is about the same as that found in fresh lean meat and fish, whereas cheese can have up to 35 per cent. Remember that fresh fruits, roots and green vegetables have negligible amounts of protein as far as the dog's nutrition is concerned, whereas dried fish and dried meat contain between 65 and 80 per cent protein which accounts for their popularity as a means of feeding dogs, since they are very palatable.

Proteins are composed of long chains of *amino acids*. Think of the protein as a bead necklace, the individual beads being the amino acids. There are altogether about 25 different sorts of amino acids, some of which are known as *essential amino acids*, since they cannot be made from others within the body. Proteins found in the muscles of fish, amphibia, mammals and birds, all vary slightly as the amino acid 'beads' are slightly differently arranged in each animal's protein 'necklace' and it should be remembered that the greater part of the organic matter of a healthy dog consists of such proteins, so it is important that protein rich food, e.g. meat, is fed to them. It should also be remembered that during digestion, proteins have to be broken down in the bowel into individual amino acids which are then absorbed and rearranged and finally combined into the particular type of protein required by the body. Soya beans contain many of the amino acids required to manufacture the type of protein found in dog muscle and this is one of the reasons that it is often combined with meat as a valuable protein source in a canine diet. Milk and eggs are also valuable sources of protein but should not be fed to excess.

Today, many commercial dog foods are directly supplemented with certain essential amino acids, in addition to combinations of vegetable and animal protein sources.

Water soluble vitamins tend to be associated with proteins just as fat soluble vitamins are associated with fats. Of the water soluble vitamins, vitamin C, ascorbic acid, is not considered necessary for the dog since it is able to manufacture its own. The B complex group, however, comprising about ten vitamins, play an important role in many of the body's functions and this is one of the reasons why yeast, a rich source of the B complex vitamins, forms a useful addition to a dog's diet.

(5) *Carbohydrates* These are fed in large quantities to dogs today, mainly because they are much cheaper than either fats or proteins and are needed in some quantities for normal utilization of fats in the body. They contain starch and sugars. Starch has to be converted into sugar in the body before it can produce energy. Man helps the process by cooking the starch which bursts the grains and makes them more easily soluble and more easily attacked by the digestive juices. It is in this way that

cereal grains, which contain more than 60 per cent of starch, can be utilized as an inexpensive addition to a dog's diet. Laboratory dogs have been fed diets of between 12½ and 70 per cent carbohydrate and have been maintained in health. Any natural starch diet (e.g. maize) is notably lacking in vitamins, minerals and essential amino acids, and consequently a natural diet, high in carbohydrates, can often be totally unbalanced for the dog, especially in respect of vitamins.

Another point worth mentioning at this stage is that foods of vegetable origin, especially whole grains, contain something called phytic acid. This tends to pass, unabsorbed, through the gut, but combines with any calcium and magnesium that may be present in the food. Therefore if foods of vegetable origin are fed to excess, any supplies of calcium or magnesium available in the diet may be depleted. In addition, any phosphorus present as phytic acid is not available because it is not digested. I think this is a factor worth remembering since growing puppies are often fed large quantities of cereals such as maize or sometimes barley and can, as a result, suffer from bone deficiency diseases, due to the lack of calcium and phosphorus although in theory plenty should be available.

Excess carbohydrate is stored in the body in the form of glycogen, or animal starch, but the body's storage capacity for this is limited, so excess starch is promptly converted into fat and this is the reaon why so many dogs, over indulged with biscuits, end up obese.

(6) *Crude fibre* This is usually supplied in the form of plant cellulose and is not digested at all in the bowel by the alimentary secretions. In the dog, unlike the cow or other herbivores, due to the shortness of the bowel there

is not sufficient time for bacterial digestion to take place and therefore, the only value of crude fibre to the dog is as a bulking agent to stimulate bowel movement. Unfortunately when veterinary surgeons speak of more bulking agents in the diet, most owners immediately fly to biscuits which actually provide more carbohydrates in the form of starch but very little crude fibre. Bran is a much better bulking agent for the dog and certainly won't make it fat and will supply it with a lot of B complex vitamins as well.

We have now looked at the major components of food and the way in which the dog uses them. Remember, however, that nutrition is a science which does not deal with food alone, but with food in relation to the animal. I think the following word picture will make this more obvious.

Imagine a field of good spring grass, in the middle of which is a bowl of raw meat. In the field there is a cow and a dog. Both the grass and the meat will contain all the six components of food we have looked at. The cow will relish the grass and will be thoroughly content but it would be completely odd if the dog started to eat this in quantity. On the other hand the dog will eat the meat, which would be an abomination to the cow under normal circumstances. Thus, it is important when considering feeding, to look at both the dog and the food together and not to pay too much attention to either at the expense of the other.

2

Digestion

In order to understand the basic principles of feeding it is essential to know a little anatomy and physiology and learn something of digestion.

DEFINITION

Digestion is the process by which food that is eaten is converted into a form that is useful and that can be

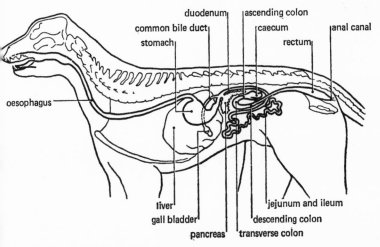

Figure 2 Digestive system of the dog in relation to anatomical landmarks

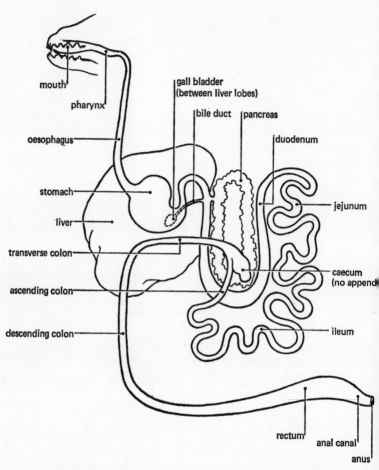

Figure 3 Digestive system of the dog (not to scale)

absorbed into the body and used to supply energy and to help replace worn out tissues. This process takes place in the digestive system, which consists of the alimentary tract and such associated glands as the liver and the pancreas.

Let us look a bit more closely at the anatomy.

Mouth As a meat eater or carnivore, the dog has teeth adapted for tearing at its prey. Unlike the grinding action of the molars (or back teeth) of man and other omnivorous and herbivorous animals in the dog there is a scissor action, as anyone who has tried to open a dog's mouth and got their fingers too far back, across the so-called carnassial teeth, will remember to their cost! Having torn at their food, dogs then tend to swallow it whole. For this, lubrication from saliva is essential and this is provided by a series of glands situated under the tongue and alongside both the upper and lower jaws. In man and other predominantly starch eaters these glands also secrete a digestive enzyme, or organic catalyst, and so digestion starts in the mouth, but in the dog it is only secreted in minute quantities and so digestion proper should not be thought of as commencing until the food reaches the dog's stomach.

Adequate supplies of saliva are essential, however, in the dog for lubrication and this was particularly important in the wild state when dogs swallowed hair and bones as well as meat. Obviously needs are greater today in those dogs fed a dry diet, compared with the soft-moist and tinned foods with up to 75 per cent water content, which can hardly be said to need much lubrication for swallowing!

Oesophagus or gullet In the act of swallowing the food passes down the tube which runs through the chest and over the heart. This is the gullet or oesophagus. It can be the site of serious stoppage or obstruction if the dog is allowed to swallow large pieces of bone or other objects. Recent programmes on space travel have illustrated very well that the entry of food into the stomach is not at all dependent upon gravity but solely on the contractions of muscles in the oesophagus. This is a process known as peristalsis and it takes place in many other parts of the alimentary tract in order that the food material can be propelled from start to finish in an orderly and precise fashion. Although objects can and do get stuck in the gullet, it is remarkably distensible and dogs will therefore sometimes swallow quite large objects like rubber bones or golf balls. Unfortunately, however, in order to enter the stomach the oesophagus has to pass through a hole in a thin muscular partition which separates the chest from the abdomen. This is the diaphragm and that hole through it is not quite so elastic and so objects sometimes get stuck at this site, the so-called cardiac valve, almost at the entrance of the stomach. They can also get stuck a bit further forward where the oesophagus makes a slight curve to pass over the heart, which can also act as a bottleneck. When this happens, the dog will endeavour to vomit, particularly after eating, but if the object is of the nature of a chop bone, it will not come back and so an oesophageal obstruction has occurred and this can be a very serious condition indeed. This is the reason why veterinary surgeons are so horrified at the thought of chop and other irregular bones being fed to dogs.

Stomach This should be thought of as 'bagpipe-shaped'. It lies on the animal's left side. Most of it is hidden underneath the ribs and it nestles closely against the liver. It is in the stomach that digestion begins in the dog. Glands are present in the lining or mucosa that produce several enzymes that are used to break down the complex proteins and also some fat. The protein splitting enzymes have to work in an acid environment and therefore there are glands present which produce a weak solution of hydrochloric acid. Another function of the stomach is to mix the food very thoroughly with these gastric juices, so that a semi-liquid mass called chyme is produced For this reason the stomach wall is very muscular. At the exit from the stomach there is a valve called the pylorus. The lining or mucosa of this part of the stomach is very sensitive. If anything hard touches it the valve tends to contract and thus try to retain the object in the stomach, rather than letting it pass through into the much narrower small intestine where a blockage can occur very easily.

Unfortunately this safety mechanism is not one hundred per cent effective and it is not unusual for dogs to have to be operated on for the removal of foreign bodies from the small intestine. However, any veterinary surgeon in small animal practice will testify to the numbers of dogs which are X-rayed for other reasons and quite large foreign objects are found in the stomach, which have been there sometimes for months and even years and not caused any trouble. My particular record is a plastic spider which measured $2\frac{1}{2}''$ in diameter, swallowed by a crossbred Spaniel two and a half years previously. The facts are accurate since the owners rushed the animal in as soon as it swallowed the spider, but nothing radical was undertaken until the dog showed signs of obstruction two and a half years later, when a very acid-scarred spider was finally removed from the intestine. In other words, that sensitive pyloric valve managed to keep that spider in the stomach for thirty months before finally losing the battle!

The small intestine This is the longest part of the digestive tract. It is roughly $3\frac{1}{2}$ times the length of the body of the dog and it is here that most of the digestion and absorption takes place. The first part of the small intestine is called the *duodenum*; it lies fairly close to the spine and is not very moveable. It is U-shaped and within the 'U' lies a gland, the *pancreas*, which plays a very important part in the digestive process. In addition, the pancreas also secretes insulin, lack of which causes 'sugar' diabetes. The rest of the small intestine is very much more moveable and hangs from the roof of the abdominal cavity, suspended by a membrane known as the mesentery. The last part of the small intestine, or *ileum*, terminates at the ileo-colic valve which is another sphincter muscle. The ileo-colic valve leads into the large intestine.

Large intestine This comprises the caecum, the colon and the rectum. The caecum is a blind sac, situated to the right, close to the spine and is quite far forward, being situated close to the pancreas in the duodenal loop. In man it ends with the appendix, but this is absent in the dog, which consequently can never suffer from appendicitis. The colon is divided into ascending, transverse and descending portions and is often very little wider than the small intestine which preceded it. It is here that fluids from the bowel contents are resorbed into the body and the faeces or excreta become solid. Once it enters the pelvic canal, the colon is called the rectum

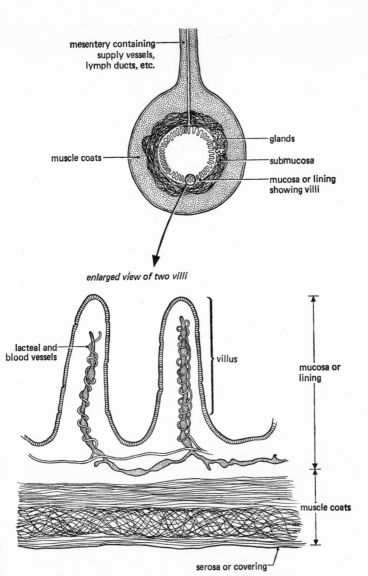

Figure 4 Cross-section of small intestine

and is the storage area. It terminates in the short anal canal which is again closed by valves or sphincter muscles which open when the animal passes motion or defecates.

The alimentary canal does not lie freely in the abdomen: it is suspended from the area of the spine by the mesenteric membranes and the amount of movement that any part of the bowel enjoys depends solely on the length and mobility of this mesentery. It is along this membrane that all the service vessels tend to get to and from the bowel. These are basically blood vessels, nerves and special vessels carrying fat called lymph vessels.

PHYSIOLOGY

Digestion is a combination of mechanical and chemical activity. The chemical activity throughout the bowel is initiated and aided by the actions of the digestive enzymes. These are complex chemicals which are produced in the cells lining the bowel and also in the pancreas and which start chemical breakdown so that complicated proteins, carbohydrates and fats are broken down into simple compounds of low molecular weight which can pass through the lining of the bowel into the bloodstream and so be transported to the liver and those tissues where they are needed. Fats also are broken up by chemical action and then split into simple compounds which are absorbed by special lymph vessels called *lacteals*. These are accommodated in millions of tiny finger-like projections called *villi* which are found in the lining of the small intestine. Their purpose is to increase the surface area of the small bowel and thus increase absorption. From the lacteals the products of fat digestion are transported via the lymph ducts but ultimately they too are discharged into the bloodstream.

The main constituents of the diet are thus broken down into simple, relatively soluble compounds: carbohydrates to simple sugars, proteins to soluble amino acids and fats to fatty acids and glycerol.

Once in the bloodstream they are distributed to those tissues that require them. Sugars are used for instant energy requirements, amino acids for the replacement of tissue and fatty acids as further important sources of energy. Excess fatty acids and carbohydrates are removed from the bloodstream by the liver. Carbohydrates are converted into glycogen, which is animal starch, and fatty acids and glycerol are converted back into fats, which are either stored under the skin or around important organs like the kidneys and the heart. The dog's ability to store glycogen is relatively poor but it can be thought of as a more immediately available food store since as soon as the animal's blood sugar level drops, glycogen is converted back into glucose and is released once more into the circulation. Fat, like carbohydrate, is composed of carbon, hydrogen and oxygen, but in fat there is less oxygen than in carbohydrate and therefore it is a much better fuel, releasing more energy, weight for weight, than does starch.

Excess food eaten is converted to fat and in the long term a dog on a restricted diet will utilize its stored fat supplies. However, during breakdown certain fatty acids can be produced which are harmful to the dog and for this reason, dogs that are starved for any reason can become seriously ill so, as with human dieting, crash diets in dogs have got to be regulated by a veterinary surgeon and should not be embarked upon lightly.

Amino acids from protein digestion cannot be stored so readily as carbohydrates and fat and therefore surplus amino acids are broken down by the liver to a substance called urea, which in turn is excreted by the kidneys. The liver's important role as part of the digestive system will now be appreciated.

Although an essential part of the diet for the growth and replacement of tissues, excess protein can result in excess quantities of urea being produced and should there be any intercurrent kidney disease, the level of the urea in the blood rises, making the animal very ill indeed and this is not uncommon in the elderly animal.

In the first chapter the role of crude fibre in the diet was discussed. Although plant fibre in the form of cellulose is not digested, its bulk does give the bowel something to work on. There is a view held by many veterinary surgeons today that many of the anal gland problems that occur in pet dogs are directly attributable to the high protein, low bulk nature of many of the prepared diets and thus the addition of some more fibre will do much to alleviate this unfortunate condition. Is it this that the dog is instinctively trying to do when it is seen 'grazing' out at exercise?

In the large intestine the resorbtion of water and many of the accumulated secretions takes place. It is also the main area of bacterial activity. Cellulose is sometimes broken down and any remaining proteins are subjected to bacterial action and it is this that results in the characteristic smell of the dog's motion. Mucus is added and the material passes into the last part of the large intestine, called the rectum and anal canal. Here the faeces, as they are now called, are stored until evacuation takes place when the dog passes motion or defecates.

Before finally leaving the subject of digestion, a few more words should perhaps be said about those two important glands, the pancreas and the liver.

As a dog grows fatter more strain is put on the joints

We end up with dogs that, like this Sheltie, are no longer healthy but fat, sluggish and often in pain

The number of different foods that dogs will eat, often avidly, is large. The three types of dishes shown are (l. to r.) stainless steel, non-tip aluminium, and spun aluminium

Following whelping the bitch will normally maintain the puppies for anything up to six to eight weeks

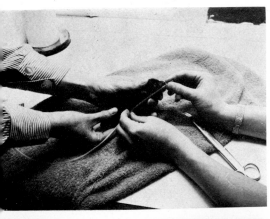

It is vitally important to measure the tube

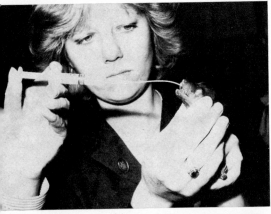

The use of too long a tube is not only inconvenient but can be fatal

The use of a correctly sized tube can be life saving

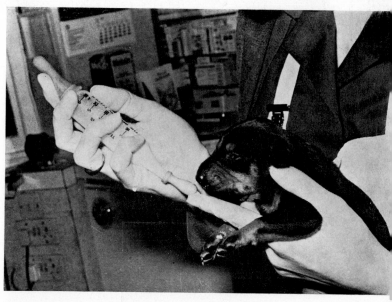

Belcroy feeding

Catac open-ended feeder in use

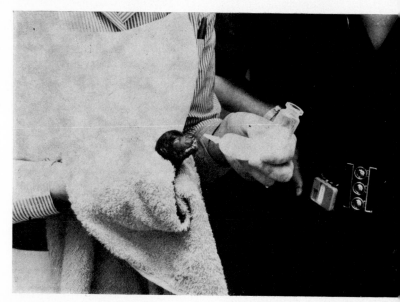

Pancreas This, as mentioned, is composed of two parts, an exocrine part which provides the pancreatic juice which passes into the duodenum and contains enzymes which digest fats, carbohydrates and proteins. Sodium carbonate is also secreted which helps to change the acidic stomach contents into alkaline small intestine contents. This alkalinity allows fats to be split into fatty acids and glycerol. The endocrine portion of the pancreas is concerned with the secretion of insulin and as such does not concern us.

Liver The liver is known as the chemical factory of the body. It is a very large organ and lies immediately behind the diaphragm in the abdominal cavity. It produces bile which contains certain secretions which result in the characteristic colour of the dog's motion. Bile also contains salts which, as emulsifying agents, aid in the digestion of fat, allowing the fat droplets to be broken down into tiny particles under the mechanical action of peristalsis.

Bile is stored in the gall bladder which is situated between the lobes of the liver, and from there, via the bile duct, it enters the duodenum. Blood from practically every part of the digestive tract passes immediately to the liver via the hepatic portal system. Liver cells then can extract the contained nutrients, store them or convert them to more readily available compounds that are in turn transported to other tissues when they are needed.

SUMMARY

The basic constituents of the food, carbohydrates, fats and protein, are, as a result of digestion, broken down into sugars, amino acids, fatty acids and glycerol all of which are transported by the bloodstream to those areas

B

where they are required. Excess sugar is stored in the liver as glycogen, while excess fatty acids are reconverted into fats and stored in specialized fat depots. Unwanted amino acids are broken down by the liver into urea, which is excreted by the kidneys, either in the form of urea or further broken down into ammonia.

3

Home-made diets versus the commercial variety

Today a dog can be fed either a home-prepared diet or one of the readily available commercial products, or a combination of both. In comparison with most human foods, commercial dog food represents a unique concept. Unlike foods prepared for human beings, commercially prepared dog food must be a complete diet; not only must all the necessary nutrients be present but the balance between one nutrient and another, and also the various vitamins etc. must be correct.

Without any doubt at all, in an inflationary situation, this is the cheapest way to feed any dog effectively.

'Non commercial' foods are simply those that have not been prepared solely for sale as dog foods. Usually 'non-commercial' dog food is home-made. It is the traditional method of feeding the pet dog. Indeed twenty-five years ago before the advent of the pet food industry, it was the only method available and certainly produced excellent stock.

Unfortunately, in most people's minds, it seems to be synonymous with the feeding of scraps and this may well have originated in Biblical times, since in the Gospel according to St Matthew one reads of 'dogs eating the scraps that fall from the table'. We have learned that the dog is a meat eater and that it can use fats very much more efficiently than starch as an energy source and so it is not difficult to appreciate that dogs could be very well fed receiving nothing but table scraps in the days before pre-packaging became paramount. Today, however, the story is different. We live in an age of pre-packaging and rising costs. With convenience foods and the popularity of portion control the accent is on total consumability, with everything prepared ready to cook. Therefore scraps tend to be rather scarce and certainly a dog could not be expected to receive a balanced diet from anything that was available from today's table. Bear in mind that I am speaking here of scraps and not of 'left-overs' from human meals.

Appetite in the dog is not a true guide to its nutrition.

A dog will eat, for example, bananas, apples and potatoes, but this does not necessarily mean that it could live healthily on such a diet. If you are determined to feed your dog solely on 'non-commercial' foods, it will cost considerably more than feeding the products of the pet food industry and I am not at all sure that you will have achieved as balanced a diet. You will also be involved in considerably more effort, because you will have to consider the balance between calories (or available energy) and available protein and this will vary according to whether you are feeding a growing puppy, a pregnant or lactating bitch, or an adult dog. At the same time, there is a balance among the nutrient elements themselves that has to be considered.

All the foodstuffs supplied to the dog are broken down into the basic simple constituents and then combined by a process known as metabolism into all the complicated compounds necessary for the animal. In order to do this efficiently, specific amounts of individual nutritional ingredients must be present and if there is a lack of any one, certain enzyme reactions will not be completed and the dog will develop deficiency diseases.

On the other hand, if there is too much of any one particular component, the dog will try to eliminate it as waste as in the case of protein, when, as we have previously discussed, the brunt of the burden falls on the liver and kidneys: or will lay down the excess to fat, as occurs when too much energy food in the form of carbohydrates or fat itself is fed. Although traditionally dogs, as carnivores, obtain their nutriment from animal sources, in preparing a home-made diet one has the freedom to choose either animal or vegetable sources. An example of this is the carbohydrate source, for although glycogen or animal starch occurs in the animal body, it is not widely available as a feeding material and therefore vegetable starch is the common form of carbohydrate incorporated into a dog's diet, although this is not a natural food for the animal and the starch must be partially broken down by cooking it. Thus although many dogs are fond of raw potatoes it should be remembered that the potato will be far more nutritious if it is cooked before being offered!

In any home-made diet the main form of carbohydrate utilized is cereal grains. These are partially cooked and ground and offered to the dog in the form of meal or biscuits and it is over-indulgence in this particular variety of food that results in so many obese dogs. It should be remembered that bread is a similar energy source and certainly wholemeal bread with its added vitamins can be particularly useful. Many breeders use bread and are often insistent that the bread should be cooked or toasted before it is offered. From a nutritional point of view, all that is essential is that the starch should be cooked and since this will have already occurred once during the baking of the bread, further baking, although it will increase the palatability, will certainly not do anything to enhance its nutritional value. It is always amazing to me how many owners will concede the fat-producing qualities of bread, but not realize that dog meal and biscuit are equally dangerous in this respect. Indeed, many owners feel that dog biscuits, being so much harder than bread, are a useful form of fibre or bulk and are not likely to result in the laying down of fat. This is totally erroneous. To provide bulk in the diet, bran in the form of All Bran or even rabbit bran, or plant cellulose in the form of cabbage stalks or similar, are probably the best methods available. Please do not use dog biscuits for this purpose.

Fats When preparing a home-made diet, animal fats are particularly useful since they can be supplied at the same time the meat is fed, often being part of it, especially if cheaper cuts are bought. Surprisingly, animal fats do not contain nearly as many essential fatty acids (or basic fat 'building blocks' if you like) for the animal as occur in vegetable oils and fat. Ordinary cooking oil, e.g. maize oil or corn oil, is a readily available and rich source of energy and also contains several essential fatty acids. These are materials that the animal cannot make itself in appreciable quantities. Because it is so rich cooking oil should never comprise more than about 10 per cent of the dog's diet, otherwise the dog will be satisfied by the oil and eat less of the rest of its food and could, conceivably, end up with a deficiency disease due to the lack of the other nutrients. Not only is the actual nutritional value of animal fats lower than the majority of the fats of vegetable origin, but just as with protein, there are variations from animal to animal, so the fat in horsemeat and also pig fat is probably more nutritious to the dog than the fat from beef or mutton, both of which almost totally lack all the essential fatty acids. Remember that from a nutritional point of view, oils and fats are the same. The only difference is that oils are liquid at room temperature.

Protein Protein sources for a home-produced diet are almost always meat dependent. Dogs have a natural appetite for meat, but do remember that meat is high in phosphorus and low in calcium and so the entirely meat fed dog, particularly if a growing animal, could soon suffer serious deficiency diseases due to the lack of calcium which would soon result in bone deformities becoming apparent. In addition, if the meat happens to be very lean with all the fat trimmed off, an entirely meat fed dog could end up dying due to lack of energy! No diet fed to a dog should contain more than 75 per cent meat. It is worthwhile considering other forms of animal protein if you are determined to produce a non-commercial diet.

Eggs are rich in proteins, vitamins, minerals and fatty acids. Eggs contain virtually every amino acid necessary for protein synthesis in the dog and virtually all the egg protein can be utilized. It is such a rich protein source that if it were the only protein source offered to the dog it would only have to be fed at the rate of about 2 oz per pound of food fed. Practically this means that if you are going to feed eggs, don't feed too many because otherwise they will be entirely wasted and not be absorbed by the animal. Raw eggs also contain a glycoprotein called avedin in the white which can combine with one of the B vitamins, biotin, and thus the feeding of excess raw eggs can lead to a serious vitamin B deficiency and ultimately to dermatitis. I personally think the ideal way of feeding eggs to a dog is to feed them cooked and whole, including the shell, which is a natural source of calcium and other minerals.

Milk is another source of protein which is especially useful in the growing dog. Its only disadvantage is that certain adult dogs can suffer from an enzyme deficiency which prevents them from breaking down the milk sugar, or lactose, into simple sugars and so diarrhoea can result if milk is fed in excess. However, if fed in quantities of, say, about 2 oz per pound of food, little trouble is likely to result and it does contain calcium and phosphorus in the correct ratio of 1.2:1.

Cheese is another useful source of animal protein, often neglected in a dog's diet. Cottage cheese contains casein, the major protein fraction of milk and its protein value approaches that of horsemeat, which is a particularly rich source of high quality protein. Ordinary hard cheese is also very rich in fat and therefore a good energy source.

Fish is another good source of protein which is often unexploited in home-made diets. Pound for pound, fish protein is an inexpensive source of high quality protein. In the raw state it contains an enzyme, thiaminase which destroys another of the B vitamins, thiamin. While discussing thiamin it is well to remember that the richest animal source is pork and it is interesting how many owners are reluctant to feed pork to their animals. Provided it is cooked it is a perfectly acceptable form of protein for the dog. Pork fat is a rich source of an unsaturated fatty acid called linolaic acid, 12 per cent of which can occur in pig fat compared with only 2 per cent in beef fat. It is lack of linoleic acid which results in the so-called fat deficiency syndrome which in turn leads to certain types of skin disease.

Unfortunately, little use has been made of vegetable

protein when compounding home-made diets. The richest source is soya bean flour which contains something like 50 per cent compared with 20 per cent in wheat grain flour, 13 per cent in peas, 75 per cent in beef. Potatoes only contain 8.5 per cent protein when fed complete with peel. Remember that if the starch content is going to be made available to the dog they must be cooked.

Having worked out the protein, carbohydrate and fat constituents of our home-made diet, we still have to provide the necessary vitamins and minerals and I think the easiest way of doing this is to buy one of the commercial balanced vitamin/mineral mixtures. The purists, however, can avoid this by feeding mixed sources of protein such as eggs, cheese, bread and fish all of which contain various vitamins and minerals, while vegetables and fruit which are included basically for their bulking content, are also rich sources of the B vitamins. Bonemeal contains calcium, phosphorus and magnesium in almost the exact ratio required by the dog. Certainly it is essential in the case of raw meat fed dogs, since these animals will be receiving a high proportion of phosphorus and very little calcium.

A useful guide in the raw meat fed dog is to provide bonemeal at the rate of ½ oz to every pound of raw meat in the dog's diet. In these animals it also fulfils another useful function in that a dog fed raw meat is receiving a high protein/low bulk diet and is frequently loose. Bonemeal often acts as a constipatory agent for these animals, but the bonemeal should not be fed to excess, otherwise chronic constipation will supervene together with a serious upset in the mineral balance we have tried so hard to achieve.

Finally, while dealing with home-made diets, I think a few words about liver would be appropriate. Among some dog owners it has achieved almost a mystical significance. I have had it quoted to me as a cure-all for fading puppies, stud dogs lacking sex drive, post-operative depression and a myriad of other complaints. Certainly it is of value. It is relished by the dog; it acts as a good laxative and it is a rich source of vitamin A. It should not be used indiscriminately or before very long the dog will have very obvious obesity problems, since it is also a rich source of energy with glycogen and fat.

COMMERCIAL DIETS

Let us now turn to the commercial diets. I was brought up in a dog breeding environment and qualified as a veterinary surgeon at a time when the commercial dog food industry was only in its infancy. It is not surprising therefore, that I, like many other breeders, grew up with a natural reticence towards commercial dog foods. However, the longer I am in practice and the longer I am personally involved with dogs, the more I realize the good sense in relying on the products of the reliable canine food manufacturers. Tremendous research and 'back-up' goes into the formulation of these diets and in terms of value for money, no home-made diet can come anywhere near them, unless you are prepared to alienate the family and immediate neighbours by cooking stinking paunch and tripe daily! All reputable manu-facturers issue feeding directions on the can or package, and although these are only intended as a guide, they are well worth studying. The tremendous obesity problems that I see daily, ofen in commercially fed dogs, would never occur if only owners would follow the manufac-turers' recommendations. I am always amazed at the number of people, often new owners with delightful puppies, who endeavour to improve upon the commercial foods being fed without really understanding the constituents anyway; obviously this can hardly result in a better product. This attitude of mind is probably just as bad as that of the other class of owner, who spurns all commercial foods and endeavours to feed their own formulae, again with little background knowledge and often, not surprisingly, with ill-balanced results. I can only hope that reading this chapter will do something to clear up these misconceptions.

Present day commercial dog foods come in a bewildering variety of forms. They are all complex mixtures of economically available ingredients which are specially blended to provide the necessary nutrients and at the same time, ensure palatability with reasonable odour and texture. They are then attractively packaged in order to appeal to the owner rather than the dog, but remember 'the proof of the pudding is in the eating' and no dog will eat food that it does not find palatable and which does not appeal to its appetite, no matter how attractive the label. However, as said previously, appetite is no indication of what is best nutritionally and the manufacturers realize this and consequently go to considerable lengths to ensure that palatability is confined to a nutritionally balanced diet.

Manufacturers, particularly those producing high protein complete diets for the adult dog, realize the pernicious habit of owners of adding to their diet and they therefore publish a guide to the feeding of the product as a complete diet alone, with nothing but water to drink; and also as a partially complete diet with biscuits and/or other energy sources added. If owners would only follow these suggestions, few of the obesity problems that are daily encountered in veterinary practice would occur. It is a silly situation that dogs are overfed and in consequence capital is expended on food which is laid down to fat, producing ill health, which in turn results in the expenditure of more capital with the veterinarian in order that the animal hopefully is restored to health, when the whole problem could be avoided at the outset by spending less money on dog food and following the manufacturers' recommendations that accompany it, in the first place.

It is in the commercial foods that vegetable proteins are more fully exploited. Remember that these do not lessen the nutritional value of the food: it is far better to feed the dog a high-quality vegetable protein, such as soya bean flour, than a low-quality animal one, such as tendons or lung tissue (lights).

There are four basic types of commercial dog foods:

(1) dry foods containing approximately 10 per cent water

(2) 'soft-moist' dog foods, containing approximately 25 per cent water

(3) canned foods containing approximately 75 per cent water

(4) specially formulated frozen foods which also contain about 75 per cent moisture

(1) *Dry dog foods* Into this category fall biscuits and biscuit meal, which are the main energy sources given even by those who spurn all commercial diets, through to complete diets containing a scientifically balanced mixture of carbohydrates, fats and proteins together with all the necessary added vitamins and minerals.

The chief function of dog meals is to balance high protein meat diets. Right from the outset biscuit manufacturers realized the low protein value of their products and endeavoured to increase this by the incorporation of meat meal and also, latterly, vegetable protein and it was in this way that complete dried dog foods gradually evolved. Evidence shows that provided there is an adequate supply of drinking water available these foods are ideal for the majority of medium and large breeds. My personal experience is that the tinies and the toys usually find them hard going and do prefer other types of commercial food. Since they only contain 10 per cent water they are considerably less bulky than the other types of commercial food presently available and in consequence are easy to store and clean to handle.

There are some disadvantages: one is the incorporation of sufficient fat to provide energy but at the same time to avoid reducing the storage life of the food. Recently, so-called 'expanded dried foods' have overcome the problem. In the manufacture of these the spraying of the food with fat at a late stage in manufacture makes it much more palatable to the animal. However, it is essential that it is correctly packed in greaseproof containers otherwise the food goes rancid and the oil soluble vitamins, A, D and E are rapidly lost. In addition, the rancid fat can cause digestive upsets. Another problem is to ensure a sufficient fluid intake by the dog. Therefore, as mentioned previously, adequate supplies of drinking water must always be provided. If you doubt that the dog is drinking sufficient, it is worth while damping the dry food before offering it.

(2) *'Soft-moist' foods* Dry foods evolved by the addition of protein in the form of meat meal to the basic biscuit mix, in order to provide an easily storable, complete diet that did not rapidly go bad. Later it was found that by adding chemicals and other preservatives to the ingredi-

ents that were cooked under pressure, the amount of water that could remain in the finished product could be increased, without leading to deterioration. These foods are known as 'soft-moist' – they allow fresh meat for example to be incorporated, and yet themselves require no refrigeration. They are clean and convenient to handle without any unpleasant odour. Since they only contain 25 per cent moisture compared with approximately 75 per cent in normal canned dog foods they are consequently less bulky and as far as the smaller breeds are concerned, are considerably more palatable than the traditional dried foods.

(3) *Canned foods* Together with biscuits, canned foods are the traditional commercial dog food. Canning is just another way of preserving wet, fresh ingredients that would readily spoil, so that they can be presented for instant use. They are available today in a bewildering variety, from contents that appear to us as highly appetizing-looking steaks in attractive jelly to brown sludge which to our eyes if not to the noses of our pets, appears most unappetizing, if not downright disgusting!

Canned foods are of two types (a) the complete balanced food and (b) the rich protein, 'meaty' types. In an age of increasing packaging costs, complete canned foods tend to be comparatively expensive when one considers they are three quarters water and the carbohydrate energy source can be packaged more economically as biscuit. However, they do contain highly nutritious protein in the form of soya expanders and fish, but due to rising costs, the tendency is to enrich these complete diets with the more expensive constituents, in other words protein. Consequently the high-protein, meaty cans are tending to dominate the market so that the main role of the canned dog food industry today depends on providing high-quality, meat protein products. These can either be used to supplement and increase the palatability of the cheaper canned foods containing mainly fish protein, or can be used to provide the protein balance in a high cereal fed diet, in other words, mixed with biscuit.

Canned foods are popular since they have a long shelf life with no need of refrigeration except when opened. The container is durable and is vermin proof. The ingredients are usually more digestible than most dried foods. The main disadvantages are the expense involved in the canning process and the fact that to get at the contents some form of can opener must be to hand.

The only true, complete canned diets today are the prescription diets, for example, convalescent diet, obesity diet and nephritis diet which are fed to the exclusion of all else and these I will discuss in a later chapter.

(4) *Frozen foods* These are specially formulated, highly digestible, very palatable and their presentation provides the nutrients in the closest to fresh form that is possible. Therefore they find tremendous favour among that section of the dog owning public who believe in 'natural' methods, although I personally would question the 'natural' nature of a compounded food which has often been minced, had fat, water and cereals added and then heated to 180°F (82.5°C) in order to kill contaminants and to break down starch grains to make them more digestible to the dog! Their major disadvantage is their need for a deep freeze for storing and the fact that they are not instantly available, since one has to wait for them to thaw out.

METHODS OF FEEDING

Due to the development of dry and semi-moist diets by the dog food industry, there are now two basic feeding programmes possible. The first is the traditional one, now known as the 'portion control' method, while the other, which depends entirely on the availability of dry and semi-moist foods and their acceptance by the animal, is the 'self-feeding' or 'ad lib' method.

The portion control method This method is useful for controlling weight gain, weight losses etc. since the owner controls the amount that is offered at any meal. Regularity is the keynote of success with this method of feeding. Dogs are creatures of habit and will thrive if fed to a regular routine at the same time each day whether this be one or more times in twenty-four hours.

My personal preference is to feed an adult, healthy dog twice daily, giving a small amount in the morning and a larger meal in the afternoon or evening. The dog should be allowed access to water at all times.

Self feeding method With this method the dog helps itself at any time to supplies of dry or semi-moist food. Adequate supplies of drinking water are even more important with this method of feeding and it must be emphasized that only complete diets should be offered, *not biscuits*. It is unfortunate that many people tend to try to compromise and offer portion feeding with the protein fraction, e.g. canned meat, and then put biscuits down for the dog to take at will. Little wonder that they ultimately invade the premises of their veterinary surgeon with an obese animal.

Theoretically, self feeding has many advantages. Eating little and often ensures that the level of nutrients in the bloodstream remains more constant and therefore the animal should maintain better condition. The ability to nibble at any time also prevents boredom and such vices as coprophagia (motion eating). When more than one dog is kept, self feeding prevents the more timid individuals from being pushed out during the 'grub stakes', since competition is entirely absent. Last but not least, in a busy household it is considerably less time consuming.

I am frequently asked if it is possible to convert adult dogs to self feeding. My answer is yes, but one has to exercise patience. My method is to continue portion feeding and introduce self feeding between the normal feeding times. If self feeding is started at normal feeding times, over feeding may occur, particularly if the dog is a greedy feeder, when he would eat as if there were no tomorrow.

With a dog that is a reasonable feeder, after a few days the amount of food fed at the regular times can be reduced and it will be found that he will readily convert to feeding himself and do this without any excesses. My experience has been that the method works well with dogs of the medium and larger breeds, with the exclusion of greedy feeders, and the conversion from one method to the other does not take too long. Indeed, we do this regularly with long-term boarders at our kennels without too many problems. I always exclude greedy feeders since they would rapidly become fat. Then one would have to curtail the supply of ad lib food which is converting the method back to portion control and so defeating the object.

Faddy feeders and also the tiny breeds do not do very

well on the dry, ad lib method in my experience, although semi-moist foods do hold great possibilities since they are largely more palatable for these smaller animals. My present experience is that all the toys and tinies do far better on the canned, meaty foods.

4

Hand-rearing –
the first six weeks

This is the first chapter dealing with the practical aspects of feeding the dog and I thought it appropriate to start with hand-rearing puppies. I hope you were not daunted by the theory in the preceding chapters, but I felt it was essential to explain the basic principles and also to give some indication of the various types of food and ingredients available, in order that we could be in a position to understand the reasons for certain suggestions for diets. In addition, armed with this knowledge, we should be in a better position to assess the value or otherwise of the odd feeding principles that are, from time to time, suggested to us.

Following a normal whelping, the bitch feeds and maintains her puppies for anything up to six or eight weeks. Provided she is adequately fed and cared for herself (and more will be said about this in a later chapter) little interference is necessary on the part of the owner. However, occasions do present themselves where puppies are orphaned or the bitch is disinclined or unable to feed them and then one is presented with the task of feeding the offspring, sometimes from birth onwards. This is *true hand-feeding*. The alternative, supplementary feeding, occurs in a situation where the bitch has inadequate milk for the size of her litter. The formulae and the principles to be adopted in both forms of feeding are really the same.

Experienced breeders each seem to have their own pet formulae for rearing the orphan puppy. Many of these are extremely complex. I remember one that consisted of duck eggs (not hen eggs, mind you!) goats milk, lemon juice, bicarbonate of soda and yoghurt. It certainly worked for the breeder in question, although I could never quite understand the reasons for the addition of yoghurt.

Unfortunately when these formulae are passed on to the novice breeder, often in a state of shock himself since disaster has struck at his first attempt at breeding, it is not uncommon for the success that the breeder has enjoyed when using them not to be repeated at the hands of the novice. This frequently leads to more upset and distress and my advice in such circumstances has always been to stick to a simple, well tried formula and if possible something that is readily available, i.e. one of the commercial products.

All the advice I offer in this chapter is based on two broad principles: my experience as someone who has owned and bred dogs since childhood; and my experience as a practising veterinary surgeon, daily meeting the problems of the novice breeder which are not always understood by breeders with more experience.

Not infrequently I am called upon to attempt to save tiny puppies that distraught owners have been trying to feed with formulae suggested by well-meaning breeders who obviously have not appreciated the lack of experience of those endeavouring to carry out the task. The task of artificial feeding is complicated by the fact that the subject is often only a few hours old and the owners have never had to undertake this sort of work before. In these circumstances, simplicity should be the keynote. Forget the complicated mixtures and use a commercial, well-tried and well-proven formula. There are several on the market today: Lactol made by Sherleys is probably the most commonly available. However, no matter what the brand I cannot overemphasize the need to follow meticulously the manufacturer's instructions as printed on the tin.

Cows' milk and human milk contain about 88 per cent water, in other words 12 per cent total solids. Bitches' and cats' milk normally contains 24 per cent total solids. If a human baby milk substitute is being used for rearing puppies or kittens, it has to be made up at about double strength in order to satisfy the offspring without 'blowing them out' with excess volume. Put another way, bitches' milk is normally twice as rich as cows' milk or human milk. Since, as we learned previously, fat is the more usual energy source in the dog, not surprisingly bitches' milk contains considerably more fat and protein than cows' milk and very much less carbohydrate. This should also be borne in mind when human-type formulae are being fed to puppies, otherwise the excess carbohydrate can result in quite serious digestive upsets. For these reasons it is always better if possible to use a bitches' milk substitute such as Lactol and the other commercially available formulae. They contain considerably more fat and protein and less carbohydrate than in the varieties available for feeding babies.

Despite all the preparations for the happy event, occasions do occur when you are caught unawares. Puppies have to be fed urgently and the shops are closed and you have no Lactol or whatever in the house. What do you do then? From the foregoing it should be obvious that evaporated milk or human baby milk substitute mixed at twice the concentration recommended for babies will be satisfactory in an emergency. Alternatively one can supplement ordinary cows' milk according to the following formula:

    fresh cows' milk – 1 pint

    single cream – 1 teacup

    egg yolk – 1

    cod liver oil – 2 or 3 drops

    sterilized bonemeal (if available) – 1 teaspoonful

A teaspoonful of gripe water can also be added if available. In over thirty years of association with rearing puppies, I have only had to resort to this formula on one occasion. Remember that if you have not a tin of evaporated milk in the house your neighbour will often be only too happy to help in an emergency. Many have young children and will have Ostermilk or another of the baby formulae readily available, which will be even better.

At birth puppies are particularly dependent upon external temperature and must be kept very warm, i.e. around 85°F (29.6°C.). Provided they are healthy, they will then live happily for twelve to twenty-four hours without needing feeding at all, by which time the shops may well be open and one can purchase a proper commercial substitute. If the bitch has undergone a Caesarean section, by that time she may have recovered sufficiently to feed them herself, which would naturally be preferable since they would then receive the colostrum or 'first milk' from the bitch. This contains many natural antibodies to protect the puppies against certain infections. It should be remembered that although commercially available bitches' milk substitutes contain correctly balanced vitamins and minerals (and in consequence one is relieved the tedium of having to add drops of this and that), it does not contain natural antibodies and if at all possible, one should try to get the puppies to suckle from the bitch for the first day or two of life, even if one has to hold them on to the bitch, so that at least they get some of this important antibody-bearing first milk. On the odd occasion in the past when we have lost a bitch giving birth, which today is happily far less common than it once was, I have been known to milk out the bitch in order that the puppies receive this important fraction of the milk. The antibodies are only produced for the first twenty-four to forty-eight hours so if the bitch is disinclined to tolerate her offspring, one does not need to persevere for more than a couple of days.

FEEDERS

Having sorted out the food, we are now left with the problem of getting it into the puppy.

There are many types of feeders on the market and most breeders have their favourites. My advice is, if it works for you, stick to it. For the uninitiated I usually advise a Belcroy feeder. This is marketed by John Bell &

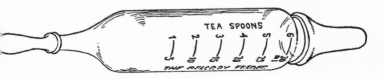

Figure 5 Belcroy tube feeder

Croyden of Wigmore Street, London W1 and is a human premature baby feeder. The teat I find small enough for all but the very tiny toys and these I will deal with separately. The only modification I make with the Belcroy is to convert the hole in the teat into a tiny slit, using a piece of razor blade, so that when the puppy sucks the slit opens and then closes as it stops. In this way the puppy takes in its own food, rather than being forced by the person doing the feeding. It is important that you do not squeeze the larger teat at the other end of the feeding bottle, but merely bend it gently with your finger if the puppy appears a bit slow.

For the really tiny puppies I use a Catac feeder, marketed by Cat Accessories Ltd of Newnham Street, Bedford. The teats supplied are very smiilar to those on dolls' feeding bottles, which are also used widely by breeders. They are much smaller than Belcroy teats. This feeder differs in principle from the Belcroy in that it is an open ended feeder and flow is controlled by the finger over the open end of the curved feeding tube. Obviously the hole in the teat should be left as a small hole and not converted into a slit.

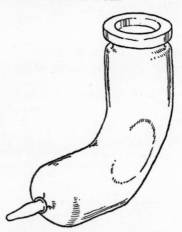

Figure 6 Catac foster feeding bottle

Other aids to hand-rearing puppies are hypodermic syringes, without a needle, and also droppers or pen fillers. These should be used with care, otherwise too much air will be taken in by the puppy during feeding, particularly if it is hungry, and then very severe colic can result.

GAVAGE FEEDING

This is a method of intragastric feeding, or feeding straight into the stomach. A piece of polythene tubing, which has been previously cut to length, is introduced into the puppy's stomach via the mouth. This is then attached to a syringe and the appropriate amount of food is then pumped directly into the puppy's stomach. Weak puppies it will certainly save, but so will the application of temperatures around the 100°F. (38°C.) mark which certainly do not require as much skill in administration! I would not recommend gavage unless you have had careful instruction from someone with experience of the method.

TEMPERATURE

The food has been organized and the means of giving it, but at what temperature should it be? Ideally, it should be at the same temperature as the puppy, around 100°F. or 38°C. In other words, lukewarm. If there is a big litter and a lot of hand-feeding to do, a baby bottle warmer is certainly an investment for keeping the milk at a constant temperature. However, I always err on the side of the milk being too cold rather than too warm if there is no accurate method of determining the temperature. Remember that many human babies today are fed with milk straight from the refrigerator in hospital and certainly suffer no ill effects. In fact, greedy feeders are considered to benefit from the feeding of cold milk since they then suck less lustily and are less likely to have colic and other digestive problems.

FREQUENCY OF FEEDING

How often? After the bitch has finished whelping, the puppies will suck continuously: they feed and sleep ad lib. With hand-rearing, one obviously wants to feed the litter often enough to ensure adequate nourishment and good growth, but at the same time to stress oneself as little as possible, particularly as far as night feeds are concerned. After years of litter rearing, I am utterly convinced that it is unnecessary to feed a healthy litter, and I stress the word *healthy*, through the night, even from birth. I realize this is somewhat contentious. It is contrary to all that has been written. One must, however, provide a warm and essentially humid environment.

Humidity is important and should be somewhere in the region of 50 per cent. This is often neglected. Remember that in their natural surroundings the bitch is continuously licking and cleaning the puppies and in consequence the ambient environment is always somewhat damp. At the same time, it is also very warm. For very young puppies, this cannot be much different from the place from which they have just emerged. If the puppies are kept in a small cardboard box, which is the commonest container, ensure that the surrounding temperature is 80°–100°F (26.8°–38°C). To ensure reasonable humidity a damp towel is quite useful, especially if infra red or other forms of electric heating are being used. At birth and shortly afterwards puppies, irrespective of their breed, are very tiny compared with their adult counterparts. Therefore the early feeding regimen must be fairly frequent; every two or three hours is certainly indicated with a last feed around midnight, when, provided the puppies are kept warm enough, they will go through to 6 a.m. when feeding can commence again. If the ambient temperature and environment is not correct I feel it would be necessary to feed during the night, but not otherwise.

A bitch, stimulated by the puppies' sucking, will continuously top and tail her offspring, licking them and cleaning up after them. When hand-rearing, you have to simulate these actions by rubbing their backs and bottoms. A small piece of cotton wool, dipped in warm water and gently rubbed along the perineal and anal regions, in other words, under the tail, will simulate mum's tongue sufficiently to ensure they defecate and urinate and do not become constipated and suffer from digestive upsets. Similarly, a finger gently rubbed along the back and belly will also stimulate burping and so prevent colic and belly-ache.

By the end of the first week, depending on the breed, feeding can be at three- or four-hourly intervals, the general rule being the larger the breed, the longer the interval between feeds. At the end of two weeks the puppies are usually beginning to lap for orphan or bottle-fed puppies are very much more advanced in this direction than those enjoying normal motherly love. Certainly by the time their eyes are open at sixteen to eighteen days, they should be beginning to learn to lap and also to take solid foods and at the same time they should be receiving approximately four or five separate feeds during the course of the day.

If the puppies have been totally hand-reared and have received no colostrum, early consultation with your veterinary surgeon is necessary in order that protection against all common diseases is provided, either by antibiotics in the case of bacterial infection or by sera and vaccination in the case of viruses. This is particularly important when there are other dogs on the premises.

SUPPLEMENTARY FEEDING

Large litters, particularly of the medium and bigger breeds, often benefit from supplementary feeding, by which one aids the efforts of the natural mother. My experience over the years as a veterinary surgeon has taught me that no bitch is able to successfully rear more than about eight puppies to a high standard without losing a lot of bodily condition, unless she has some form of help in the form of supplementary feeding. This ensures there is less strain on the bitch and consequently she is not pulled down so much by the pregnancy and subsequent lactation. The same procedure is followed as with total hand-rearing. Puppies are fed at frequent intervals but are given back to the bitch in between so they can suck as necessary. Care should be taken to ensure that all the puppies actually do suck and the smaller ones do not get pushed out in the scramble for the milk bar. Remember that the smaller and weaker the puppy, the more it will benefit initially from the protective action of the colostrum and should not be allowed to be pushed out in the fight for food. It helps tremendously if you just hold these tiny puppies on to the teats so they can at least suck their share, if not their fill, which can be then arranged by judicious supplementation.

Normally, milk production increases in the first three weeks following whelping and represents adequate nutrition for the puppies during this period of life. After three weeks the nutritional requirements of the puppy continue to increase, but milk production in the bitch decreases and this is the period of weaning which will be dealt with in the next chapter.

I have purposely dwelt at length on the question of rearing the orphan puppy, or neonate, since if this task is correctly carried out, one has a basically sound product which will grow and benefit from the rest of the feeding suggestions contained in this book. If the orphan puppy is injudiciously or incorrectly fed, however, irreparable damage can be done which will affect it for the rest of its life.

5

Weaning

Weaning is the transition process through which the puppy has to pass between the ages of about four to eight weeks. It is a very critical period in a puppy's life in which the digestive system has to be educated to accept nutrients that have not been offered previously. Remember that before the puppy is born, while developing in the uterus, it has been fed via the placenta on pre-digested food from the mother. Once birth has occurred in normal circumstances, it has relied upon easily digestible nutrients found in the mother's milk which is taken on an almost a continuous basis for the first three weeks of its life. Ultimately, when adult, being a carnivore, it will eat a mainly meat diet and hopefully, provided the owners are not overindulgent, it will be fed only once or twice in twenty-four hours.

When weaning commences, a variety of solid foods is going to be offered. Obviously this involves major digestive reorganization by the puppy. At the same time dramatic physiological and neurological developmental changes are taking place. This is the beginning of the critical period of 'socialization' which can markedly affect the puppy's future behaviour patterns with respect to man, its environment and also to other dogs. Thus the weaning period is an extremely important one for the puppy and if incorrectly undertaken, the animal frequently can suffer the effects for the rest of its life, not only from the point of view of digestion but temperamentally as well.

It should be remembered that the breeding and rearing of puppies is a specialized business, particularly if those puppies are intended ultimately for the pet market. For example, incorrect handling during weaning, particularly in the highly strung or nervous breeds, can often markedly alter a puppy's attitude towards strangers for the rest of its life. The fact that this incorrect handling is the result of inexperience is really no excuse. In the more nervous breeds, gentle but determined socialization with a lot of different human contacts is essential during the weaning period. In this way, much of the reserve and nervousness will be overcome and the animal will make a satisfactory pet.

The bitch's milk starts to decline at about the third week, whereas the needs of the puppy continue to increase. Most books therefore suggest that weaning should commence about this time but I personally feel, particularly in the case of the pet puppy, that weaning cannot be started too early. My general rule is to start the weaning as soon as the eyes are open, from about the sixteenth day.

· Early weaning always seems to be the pattern for hand-reared puppies and it may well be that there is less change between the formula with which they have been bottle fed and the formula they are given to take themselves by lapping. My method is to make this transition stage as smooth as possible, so I start weaning by feeding the bitch one of the simulated bitches' milk substitutes, in the bed with her puppies. I feed her in a shallow dish and as the puppies come toddling up, I stand them in the dish and touch their noses with my finger dipped in the milk, in order to get them to lap. Most bitches will tolerate this procedure, although some will object to the puppies going anywhere near their food supply. I frequently wonder if these bitches have had sufficient supplies of food during their pregnancy or lactating period, or alternatively whether they themselves were properly weaned. None of my own bitches has ever objected to this procedure and these have included Bassets and Wire Haired Terriers that are not among the easiest of animals to handle when they have a litter!

Remember puppies are social animals. In the majority of cases they will soon learn to lap by copying mum. Some authors recommend dunking the mouths into the fluids but I feel that this is a traumatic procedure and is hardly conducive to teaching the puppy that feeding is a pleasant sensation.

If the bitch shows any signs of restlessness at the puppies taking her food, I withdraw them and persevere by teaching them to lap by hand. The biggest and most advanced members of the litter usually cotton on to the feeding process rapidly and are then in turn used to teach the slower members of the family. In the meantime these are being fed from the bitch but it is also a good idea to supplement them, since this will get them used to the same mixture they will take when they start lapping.

Once it has learned to lap, the next stage is to get the puppy to eat solids and for this I find that raw scraped meat in tiny quantities, placed in the mouth from the fingers, is by far the best method. The taste of raw meat seems to induce the puppies to chew very rapidly and as soon as this occurs, they can then be offered cooked meat or any of the puppy meat diets. For ones that are slow, I tend to use the meaty baby foods for a couple of days, before gradually moving them to either cooked, minced

Weaning is a critical period in the puppy's life, during which a gradual transition from milk to meat takes place

If bones are fed at all they must be large, fresh and unsplinterable. This big marrow bone is ideal

Never offer chicken bones

Overweight and pregnant – 'mated for her own sake'

In an urban Small Animal practice approximately 75% of all dogs
presented are to some extent obese

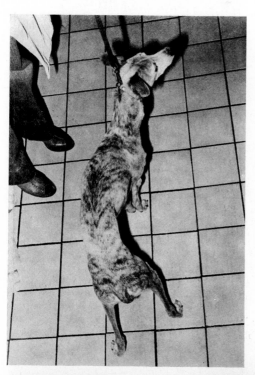

Kennel stress. This whippet was eating very well and losing weight daily

The same dog back home ate less but rapidly regained its lost weight

meat or Pedigree Chum puppy food or something similar.

It is important to remember that as young carnivores, puppies' standards are very different from our own and therefore they will often take and relish mixtures which, by our standards, are revolting and nauseating in the extreme. For example, I will mix tinned dog food with milk and eggs, making a slurry which the puppies will slurp down with tremendous satisfaction. In this way they are getting sufficient energy from the carbohydrates and fats present in the milk and at the same time are receiving meat protein, upon which they will ultimately depend, mixed in a form which is not too foreign to them, since they have been used to milk for the first weeks of their life. Eggs, provided they are not used to excess, ensure that all the essential amino acids are provided.

Assuming the puppies' eyes have opened at fourteen to sixteen days, by eighteen to twenty days they should have started lapping and at around three to three and a half weeks they should be eating. By this time they are starting to cut their deciduous or milk teeth and natural weaning in many breeds will be taking place anyway, because the more lusty puppies, with their forceful sucking, will be hurting the bitch with their teeth and gums and she will be becoming more restless and want to leave them. This is then a good opportunity to supplement, both with milk substitutes and meaty foods. I waste no opportunity in offering the puppies food when the bitch has voluntarily left them. In highly maternal bitches who resent the presence of anyone around, such periods can usefully be used to carry out the weaning process with less stress both on the puppies and the bitch.

Early weaning is especially important in those breeds

C

that normally have a lot of mammary development and also in the case of show bitches, since they will return to show condition very much sooner than if left to wean the litter naturally, which will probably not take place until the puppies are six to seven weeks old. By four and a half weeks, I try to have the puppies practically independent of the bitch except at night, and by five and a half weeks I start to encourage the bitch to stay away at night as well and then let her go back only two or three times during the day for a few minutes only. In this way the bitch's milk dries up naturally and the puppies are self supporting when they leave mum at six weeks or shortly afterwards.

Four important things are established by these procedures.

(1) The weaning process is hastened because the puppies are fed independently of the bitch from an early stage of development.

(2) Socialization and humanization of the puppy is taking place by handling and I would stress that it is always a good idea to get as many people as possible to handle and play with the puppies at this period of development if they are intended as pets, but in this I do not include very young children since they can inadvertently hurt and frighten puppies and this obviously does more harm than good in the learning period.

(3) The bitch's intake of food can be adjusted as necessary: reduced in the case of the fat bitch, increased in the case of the thin, over-maternal animal, who is giving all to the puppies.

(4) The puppies are being fed a diet that is more suitable for them than the bitch's food, which they would start to eat if they were allowed to wean naturally.

It is quite normal at about this time for some bitches, particularly the nervous, highly maternal types, to start vomiting shortly after a meal, often promptly eating the food once more. This is often a sign of natural weaning, when the bitch will eat her fill, away from the nest, and go back to vomit, in order that the puppies should start to eat some partially digested food. Although normal in the wild state, this often causes concern to the novice breeder, and many bitches are given treatment for 'gastritis' which is really only a sign of a normal maternal behaviour pattern.

How much food to give? This is a difficult question to answer; it depends on the size of the individual, the breed and the age. Remember three important points:

(1) For the first three weeks or so of its life the puppy has relied on milk, at first continuously and later intermittently.

(2) The puppy is much smaller than its adult counterpart and considerably more active.

(3) It is growing, rapidly at first and then more slowly, as it approaches six months of age.

From these facts, a satisfactory feeding programme can be evolved:

Meat and milk We have seen that the diet is basically meat and milk, with more milk at eight weeks of age, whereas at six months of age it will be more meat protein than milk.

Frequent meals At six weeks give about six or more meals, gradually decreasing, while increasing the quantity as the puppy's capacity grows so that at six months it will be having two meaty meals a day with a milk food drink in the morning. This can be later reduced to one meal a day when the puppy is adult. This again will depend on the rate of maturing common to the breed. For example,

giant breeds really need extra nourishment until they are
fifteen to eighteen months old.

Low bulk, high calories Low bulk, high energy, highly
nutritious food is necessary since at this age the capacity
of the stomach is small compared with the adult and it is
undergoing a period of great activity: lean meat and
milk concentrates at six to twelve weeks increasing the
bulk in the form of more roughage as growing slows
down. Compared with bitches' milk, cows' milk is high
in carbohydrates and low in protein and can be offered
at about this time. Vitamins and minerals, especially
vitamins A and D, calcium and phosphorus must be
added during this period as the puppy grows.

WORMING

Roundworms are especially important in dogs since one
of them, Toxocara canis which, with Toxascaris leonina,
is found commonly in puppies and has been found
occasionally to cause disease in children, also causes
problems in the dog. Every effort should be made therefore to control infection, although this is not easy due to
the particular life cycle of the worm. Unlike tapeworms,
both Toxocara canis and Toxascaris leonina complete
their development without having to pass through
another animal or 'secondary' host. Puppies can therefore
easily become re-infected by eating infected larvae that
have been passed out in the motions. These larvae, or
juvenile worms, before developing into egg-laying
adults in the bowel of the host, undergo a fairly complicated maturation process, once they have been swallowed,
migrating through the tissues of the body of the animal.
The actual pathways vary according to the age of the
puppies, and some of the larvae remain encysted in the

tissues and only complete their development as the result of some stimulus at a later date. In the bitch, pregnancy acts as just such a stimulus, and this causes the encysted larvae to start to migrate through the tissues once more,

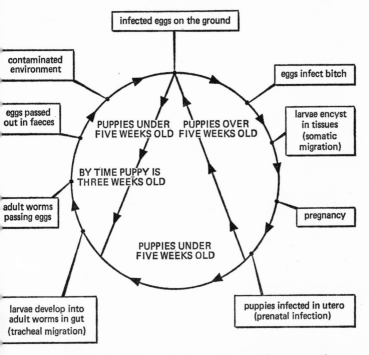

Figure 7 Life cycle of the common roundworm (*Toxocara canis*)

and after about the forty-second day, they can cross the placenta and infect the unborn puppy. Once in the puppy, the larvae follow a fixed pattern of migration which includes passing through the lungs and ultimately they arrive in the bowel where as mature worms they can be producing eggs which are passed out in the puppy's motion as early as twelve days after birth. Such extensive migration in a tiny puppy can cause damage the clinical signs of which are pneumonia, and other lung problems as well as diarrhoea, vomiting and colic, apart from the classical pot-bellied appearance.

One of the questions I am frequently asked is where the puppies get the worms from in the first place and once it is realized that the larval worm can pass across the placental barrier, the old wives' tale regarding worms being acquired from raw cows' milk and other sources are no longer creditable.

Once on the ground, the eggs, which are too small to be seen with the naked eye, are easily carried from place to place, since they have a sticky shell and are remarkably resistant to all the normal disinfectants. The only sure way of destroying eggs on the ground is to use a flame gun on them.

It is these remarkable properties that present the dangers to children, who can easily transfer these microscopic eggs from their hands to their mouths after playing in areas where dogs normally pass their motion.

Since disinfection of the places where dogs defecate is so difficult, control via elimination of worms in the dog is the obvious line of attack, but this is in itself difficult since modern worm remedies kill only the adult worms in the bowel. What is required is an effective larvaecidal agent to kill the juvenile worms in the tissues and until we have this, we cannot hope easily to produce worm-free puppies.

With this in mind, the Clinical Studies Trust Fund, which is the veterinary profession's own charity, administered by the British Small Animals Veterinary Association, is presently financing research to find such a drug that will kill these migrating juvenile worms. Remember when you see a CSTF collecting box, that this is the sort of practical work the money goes to finance and give generously. It is a worthwhile cause!

How then can we tackle the problem with our present drugs? Firstly, puppies should be wormed early. Remember they can be passing eggs by the time they are twelve days old. I start worming at three weeks and since the larvae in the tissues are maturing all the time, I worm weekly until they go to their new homes at six to eight weeks old. At the same time, don't forget that the bitch is continuously mopping up after the puppies and therefore re-infesting herself so it is worth while also worming her at the same time that the puppies are wormed, although it must be remembered that some of the juvenile worms developing in her tissues are going to encyst until the next pregnancy occurs.

When puppies are presented for inoculation, I suggest monthly worming until six months old and then two or three times a year, particularly if there are young children in the family.

Many effective remedies are available on free sale from pet shops but I think it is still worth considering consulting your veterinary surgeon for not only will he prescribe the correct dose for the puppies which sometimes can be difficult to estimate, but will also often prescribe a completely different drug to be used on the bitch.

6

The town dog

The majority of dogs kept as pets in this country can be classed as town dogs and therefore for the majority of my readers this will probably be the most important chapter of this book.

Gone are the days when dogs were kept outside and had to exist on what they could find for themselves, plus the odd table scraps. They were usually underfed and as such were considered to be better guards, just as the hungry cat was always considered to be the better mouser! They were certainly not under-exercised for sheer hunger forced them to go on foraging expeditions, sometimes for quite long distances. With the rise in living standards, dogs have now moved from being underfed guards to overweight, overfed, pampered pets. How has this happened?

Their whole lifestyle has changed to accommodate them to the artificial environment we have created for them. Unfortunately, many of these dogs are still under-nourished since they are often fed quite the wrong kind of food.

Most dogs are now kept entirely within the house and are only let out at regular, or sometimes highly irregular intervals, in order to perform their natural functions, often in a postage stamp sized back garden. A great many get no more exercise than this. In fairness, my experience has taught me that even the most conscientious owner will frequently totally underestimate the exercise needs of his pet. Often the owner of a dog such as a lusty Labrador will, on questioning, tell me he goes to the park two or three times a day at most. After much discussion this usually turns out to be two or three miles of exercise a day. When the intake of energy foods is accurately determined, most owners are dumbfounded to find that the animal should really be doing about twenty-five miles per day, if its weight is to remain stable! This establishes the first point I wish to make. Food intake depends largely upon the exercise level and can vary enormously. Dogs that have the freedom of a large garden can often eat twice as much without any obesity problem as the same size dog that is only let out two or three times a day to be clean.

A dog that lives exclusively indoors is probably one of the least active animals in the world today. It is considerably less active than its owner, it doesn't even have to walk about to prepare its food or to clean its house since its indulgent owner does everything for it. The dog spends the majority of its life sleeping, waking only at meal times in order to walk a few yards to its feeding place, and then perhaps twice that distance into the garden in order to relieve itself. Probably as a direct result of the pace of modern living, I feel sure that this class of animal is increasing in numbers. The number of owners who, when questioned about exercise for their pets, tell me rather shamefacedly that they have been 'a bit busy recently' is, to me, worrying. It is a difficult problem for these people are not in any way wishing to deprive their animals. After all, they bring them to the veterinary surgeon when they realize that something is the matter, but often then it is too late. The damage has been done.

With this in mind, the British Small Animal Veterinary Association, in conjunction with Pedigree Petfoods Ltd, the largest manufacturer of canned commercial dog foods in this country, launched a campaign of 'responsible petmanship'. It suggested that it is irresponsible to select a dog as a pet if one's lifestyle is such that the animal cannot be exercised properly. Equally, one should not select a breed that will require a high exercise level if there is no possibility of coping with this. Remember, the under-exercised dog is the bored dog and is then looking for food and so becomes the obese dog.

Obesity is the main underlying cause of many of the conditions seen in small animal practice every day. When I comment on a dog's obesity, in eight cases out of ten the stock reply is, 'Oh, it's not for what he eats'. I am at a loss to think of any other reason that could put weight on the animal, despite the fact that most owners will try to cling to some obscure glandular imbalance or 'his thyroid'. I point out that it is undeniably true that there were no fat people in Nazi concentration camps. In other words, if food is not available, obesity, no matter what its cause, will not be present either. Do not think, however, that I am suggesting that our canine companions should be starved. The only plea I make is that they should be fed rationally and intelligently.

A dog that is reasonably exercised and not bored will only eat the amount of food needed to meet its individual calorific requirements. At the same time, appetite is no indication of nutrition, as I have said several times before. In other words, a dog will eat to fulfil its calorific needs, but will not necessarily eat adequately to nourish itself. With the bored house pet, eating becomes the only pleasurable activity left to the animal and often gluttony supervenes. Unfortunately this is mistaken by the owner for hunger and consequently more food is given, often in the form of energy-rich titbits. Hence, the animal eats more, becomes more obese and therefore is even less inclined to take exercise because its limb joints now start to ache due to the weight burden. Hence a vicious circle is quickly established. Most owners on seeing this will very quickly fly to the solution of more exercise, not realizing that forcing this unfortunate dog to take exercise against its will can often do more harm than good, as I mentioned in the opening chapter. The obese, lazy, overfed dog, can if one is not careful, end up an orthopaedic cripple with heart and respiratory problems thrown in for good measure, all as a result of the owner's good intentions.

I consider that part of the pleasure of dog owning is the ability to indulge yourself by spoiling your dog from time to time if you feel like it, and the odd titbit, the odd sweet, does not harm the dog. Unfortunately the majority of urban dog owners appear hell-bent on a course best entitled 'Let's kill Rosie with overindulgence'. This classic situation is not only ridiculous but ultimately brings much heartbreak. It is also totally preventable.

What happens? Usually when the owner is eating, either at meal times or in between, he gives the dog a sweet or a titbit. Often when he is eating, he drops the odd bit off his plate for the dog. Unfortunately, he fails to realize that he sometimes weighs ten times as much as his pet. Imagine what would happen to him if he ate ten times as many sweets or treats as he is giving his dog. I try to put this another way when confronted by owners who are unable to accept that their animals are overfed. I suggest that over a twenty-four hour period they honestly write down or put on a plate an equivalent amount of everything that the dog has been given. I then suggest the owner does the same thing with his own twenty-four hours' intake and then he compares the two, and also compares them in relation to the difference in his weight and the dog's weight. Usually, without further explanation, the point is made.

Titbits, however, do have a place. The established routine of reward when an animal has completed any training task satisfactorily is a good one and gains very rapid results.

From the previous chapter, I think it is obvious that I favour the well balanced commercial products for dog feeding. When I put this to owners who come to me asking for advice on feeding, I am surprised at the number who assume a look of total horror and either say, 'Oh, he won't eat that' or 'I never feed tins'. A large proportion of these people have never really tried any of the products that are under discussion. Another point often made to me is that such a diet would be boring: that the dog appreciates variety. I do not think this is true at all. Rapid changes from one diet to another or even from one brand of food to another can lead to digestive upsets since the bacteria in the bowel become stabilized when one particular food is fed and can become drastically upset if there is an alteration in the diet. Many vomiting and diarrhoea episodes that are seen by veterinary surgeons as an everyday occurrence are often due to well meaning efforts on the part of owners to provide their pets with a little variety. This desire for a little variety has also led the petfood manufacturers to produce their products in such a bewildering variety and I am quite sure that this is not really appreciated by the dog. Once you have found a food that suits the animal, provided it is balanced and fed in the correct quantity, stick to it and feed it the *correct* quantity. What could be simpler?

Because the dog is a carnivore, we naturally assume that he is entirely a meat eater and often well meaning folk feed meat at the expense of all else. If fresh meat is fed, the dog can often end up with a deficiency disease since meat is high in phosphorus and low in calcium, as we have already mentioned. Why does this not happen in the wild? Normally the wild dog will kill herbivores for food and usually eats the intestines, stomach and offal first. He is thus provided with plentiful carbohydrates in the form of partially digested starch which the herbivore has taken in from the plants it has eaten and has, itself, partially digested. The dog next consumes the muscle meat and then the bone and in this way he gets the correct proportions of calcium and phosphorus.

Probably the most palatable of all the commercial dog foods are the meaty varieties and for the normally exercised dog that is not overweight these should be offered as a balanced diet mixed with some biscuit, to provide the energy and also a certain amount of bulk in the form of fibre, otherwise the high protein, low bulk nature |of the canned products will tend to cause diarrhoea and/or constipation and can also be responsible for anal gland problems as well. If a low energy intake is required, meaty canned food can be mixed with some bran which acts as a bulking agent.

PORTION CONTROL FEEDING

Most town dogs are fed on a portion control basis and I am frequently asked how much should be fed. There are various rough guides, such as half an ounce per pound body weight, but total intake depends on activity, size, age, physical makeup, temperament and environment.

For example, in our centrally heated houses, dogs now need considerably less food in winter than previously, when they used quite a lot of energy to keep warm. With so many variables, it is impossible to prescribe an exact amount for any particular animal; it can only be determined by trial and error. If the dog seems to be putting on weight, reduce its intake and vice versa. Even the frequency of feeding appears to cause some divergence of opinion among the experts. Some say that all adult dogs should receive two meals a day, while others, the nutritionalists of Pedigree Petfoods among them, suggest only one meal.

Smaller breeds, i.e. those under ten pounds in weight, have a higher metabolism and therefore require more food, pound for pound, than the large or giant breeds and these I always tend to feed twice a day, while the bigger breeds very adequately maintain on just one meal every twenty-four hours, with probably a drink and a biscuit or other titbit at the opposite end of the working day.

Try to standardize the time and place of feeding. The dog will then learn to eat only at that place and at that time and if the pattern is not broken by giving titbits, you will never be bothered at the meal table.

AD LIB FEEDING

The majority of town dogs can benefit from the ad lib feeding of a complete diet, be it dry or semi-moist, provided this is not interfered with in any way, for if other forms of food are also given, the balanced nature of the diet is destroyed and obesity and other problems can result. These foods contain a higher proportion of fibre than canned meaty foods and this appears to help those dogs with recurrent diarrhoea problems, presumably because the food now contains sufficient bulk to make a soft formed stool. In order to further achieve this, many of these commercial foods contain pectin which absorbs water and retains it in the faeces and thus the chances of either constipation or diarrhoea are both reduced. Vegetable pulp is a rich source of both pectin and fibre and if tomato pulp is used, as is often the case, carotine and vitamin E are also present. The vitamin E can undergo chemical changes to provide further vitamin A. It is for these reasons that one can find tomato pulp an ingredient of a particular commercial diet being fed.

In conclusion, I would stress that the preferences and prejudices of the owner should not take precedence over the need for good health in the urban dog. It should be remembered that few dogs will starve themselves, but at the same time, a dog's appetite is no indication to what is nutritionally best for him. If any adjustment or change of diet is necessary, it will be easier for all concerned if a gradual weaning process from the ill-balanced previous diet on to the new diet is undertaken, rather than just offering a bowl of some completely strange food to the dog and expecting him to wolf it up in his usual way. He won't!

7

The show dog

Puppies intended for a show career must be fed correctly from weaning, since errors in feeding at this time can result in irreversible changes and no amount of good food later on will correct these. Remember too, that irrespective of how well bred the puppy might be, the ultimate conformation and general condition of the dog in the show ring depends to a large extent on this feeding programme. An example will make this clearer. I well remember a novice Labrador breeder who, on my advice, spent as much money as she could possibly afford to secure a good puppy for show purposes.

Enthusiastic and conscientious, she discussed her puppy with all and sundry and upon hearing from an experienced handler that 'raw meat was the best food for her puppy', she fed this to the exclusion of all else. Not cheap raw meat, mind you, but the best steak she could obtain! We have already discussed feeding dogs meat and nothing else. You will know what happened. The puppy grew but rapidly developed deficiency diseases similar to rickets and so despite all the care and cost involved this lovely puppy developed irreversible bone changes and was useless for show purposes.

I still see her today, although she is now an old Labrador. It is to the owner's eternal credit that she is not an old, fat Labrador, for I impressed upon her after these irreversible changes had occurred that there would be a greater possibility of arthritis developing in the misshapen joints as the dog aged and in consequence the owner has been particularly careful not to let her put on weight. Nevertheless, even at ten years of age, her misshapen joints still bear mute testimony to the fact that appetite is no guide to an animal's nutrition.

Just as with pet dogs, people involved with show dogs seem obsessed with the necessity to provide variety in the animal's diet. Dogs are creatures of habit and provided they are eating a balanced and complete diet *there is absolutely no need for change*. Often changing the diet will upset the animal and certainly if the quality of the protein is drastically altered, e.g. feeding beef one day and pork another, allergic upsets can occur if the dog happens to be at all sensitive to any of the meat proteins. I advise feeding a good commercial diet but the most common objection I hear is that 'the dog won't eat it'. This I challenge because it is not my experience except in a very small percentage of cases. Provided the new food is introduced gradually and not suddenly presented to the animal to the exclusion of all else, little trouble occurs in acceptance. Some breeds, notably Bassets and Labradors, are easy; they are greedy feeders and eat anything and everything in sight, whereas others, particularly those of a nervous or highly strung nature, will tend to be more difficult to feed and will require much more patience to get them to accept any change that is prescribed.

The feeding of the show dog really differs little from the feeding of any other type of dog. It depends on how you start off. If at weaning you tend to pander to the animal's whims and because he won't eat one thing, promptly substitute another, then often you have a faddy, difficult feeder on your hands for life.

Remember dogs are different from people.

In their natural state dogs hunting in packs will often make a kill and gorge themselves and then rest for two or three days before embarking upon another hunting expedition, which may last several days before a kill is made. Therefore their digestion is geared to irregular feeding habits much more than ours. Certainly no harm is going to come if food is refused for twenty-four hours or even forty-eight hours. However, I do concede that some animals are difficult to keep in tiptop show condition because their eating habits are capricious and these animals can present headaches. This happens mainly among the smaller breeds and the toys. Unfortunately it is these animals that lose their show condition much more quickly if they do not eat. It is therefore not unreasonable for owners of these animals to fly to hand-feeding and to titbits, but this also presents problems since top show condition depends on a correctly balanced diet and the possibility of this becomes remote when titbits have to be resorted to. I am often consulted about some little white hope for the championship circuit who will only eat meat and won't touch biscuits or anything else. Obviously, this presents problems as far as energy requirements are concerned but remembering what has been said about fat being the most efficient form of energy food for the dog, I usually suggest to worried owners that they try feeding fatty meat, in othe words, buy scrag end or neck of mutton rather than best steak. Another good tip with these meat eaters is to put a spoonful of corn oil with the meat diet, since maize or corn oil, apart from providing energy, also provides some unsaturated fatty acids, particularly linoleic and linolenic, which will help to maintain the animal in good coat and skin condition.

Oil is biochemically fat, but it should be remembered that the fat should not exceed by more than 10 per cent by weight of the animal's diet, otherwise the calories taken in by eating this oil will dull the dog's appetite even further and so it will not take so much meat and then a vicious circle will be set up, which could end in a disastrous deficiency problem.

During my career with dogs I have tried various types of diet over the years and I am now utterly convinced that the ideal feeding regimen for the show dog should be commenced at weaning and should consist of one of the complete diets, be it a canned food, a dry food or a soft-moist. Whether the animal is fed on a portion control basis once or twice a day, or ad lib, which remember does essentially mean 'at pleasure', does not matter one jot. It depends very much on breed and domestic circumstances and environment.

Ad lib feeding in my hands, with Bassets, has been totally disastrous. They would stand at the feed bowl and eat until it was empty and if it was re-filled, they would stand there and eat until it was empty again. On the other hand, I know of several colonies of Beagles that have been reared on dry food and received nothing else but water in unlimited quantities and have been in fine condition and have reared puppies successfully.

When using commercial diets to feed the show dog, I cannot over-emphasize the need to follow the manufacturer's recommendations. Little good and considerable harm will be done by supplementing with biscuits or other bits and pieces. The chances are the animal will put on weight and lose condition.

Two important relationships in the nutritional balance of any dog food become of paramount importance when feeding for show condition.

(1) One is the balance between energy in the form of calories and protein in the form of body building materials. The protein must be of high quality and when feeding commercial canned diets, it is essential that the better quality canned dog foods from reputable manufacturers are purchased.

(2) Relationships exist between the nutritional elements themselves and this is the reason for the need for caution if the animal is being supplemented.

Some dogs do lose condition when they are being shown, often due to stress, and if judges comment that the dog should be carrying more weight, I would suggest supplementing with corn oil or fat or adding dog biscuits if the dog likes these. Use a wholemeal biscuit for the B vitamins they contain. Additionally, buy a type that is acceptable to the dog, not only from the point of view of taste, but whether or not it agrees with the animal. Most biscuits today have some added protein in one form or another and this can cause, in some cases, allergic reactions in susceptible animals. These manifest themselves either by the dog itching and scratching or sometimes having bowel upsets. Neither is required in the show dog!

Obviously the addition of some meaty foods will frequently tempt a reluctant feeder but do remember that the addition of meat protein on its own will do little to increase the animal's weight, since most of its energy requirements come from the fat and carbohydrates that it eats. However, the addition of meat will often sharpen the dog's appetite for the rest of the food being offered.

Minerals are another important consideration particularly in the show animal. Bone products are the chief sources of calcium and phosphorus which, as we have seen, should be fed at a ratio of approximately 1.1 calcium to 1 phosphorus. On a dry matter basis, diets should contain about 0.6 per cent calcium and 0.5 per cent phosphorus although the requirements of the individual animal obviously vary according to its age and status.

Puppies and pregnant or lactating bitches require more.

Whether bones should be fed to show dogs, or for that matter to any dog is a matter of opinion, opinion that is strongly divided, among breeders, dog owners and veterinary surgeons alike. As a result of my experience of the problems they can cause. I would certainly never give them to my dogs, although obviously I use bone products in the form of bonemeal.

Many breeders and owners of show dogs, however, rely on bones to relieve boredom, preferring the animal to chew at a bone than to chew at itself, which often happens. Another reason that is given to me for feeding bones is that it is in this way the dog receives natural calcium and phosphorus. My answer is that equally natural is sterilized bonemeal which certainly will not cause as many problems. If the dog wants to chew something, what is the matter with a beef hide or similar chew that cannot be splintered or cause possible trouble? In any case, if a balanced diet is being fed, such supplementation should not be necessary. If bones really must be fed, then they should be of the large marrow variety and should be fed raw. When they are chewed and contaminated they should be thrown away. If the bones are cooked, the proteins, vitamins and a large amount of the goodness in the marrow are leached out during the cooking and the bone becomes softer. When the dog gnaws it, it crumbles and the fine 'bone sand' can cause constipation or even obstruction. Frequently dogs are presented with something similar to concrete in their large bowel as a result of this practice. Another bad practice is feeding bones with a lot of meat attached. The dog certainly likes it but in the summer it soon becomes contaminated and can lead to all sorts of digestive upsets.

8

The working dog

From the theory of nutrition dealt with in the early chapters, we are now in a position to appreciate that the working dog, expending energy during its activity, requires a higher proportion of energy foods, (i.e. fats and carbohydrates) in its diet than its more sedentary counterpart. The only other nutrient required in greater proportion than in the normal diet is protein which should be present in a highly digestible form in the diet of those dogs that have sustained periods of work, i.e. gun and hunting dogs, sled dogs or the very active guard dog, in order to make good the losses sustained by wear and tear on the muscles due to the prolonged activity. Protein needs in the case of working dogs such as sheepdogs or racing Greyhounds are comparatively small since these animals only have sustained levels of hard activity for very short periods and thus the protein content of the normal maintenance diet should be able to cope.

If working dogs are fed the same balanced diet as pet animals, in order to consume sufficient to cover their energy needs, they will eat excess quantities of protein and the other nutrients, in order to ensure sufficient fats and carbohydrates. If their work load is particularly heavy they may be just not capable of eating sufficient food to cover all their energy requirements in the time allotted to them between their working periods and therefore, as often happens with working dogs, they will lose weight and condition. Therefore nutritionalists, when talking about the diet of working dogs, say they must have food of high calorific density, in other words a lot of calories in a small volume. Equally, the protein fraction of their diet must be protein of high digestibility, i.e. good quality muscle meat, rather than tendon which is only poorly digested.

The feeding of the working dog will obviously depend on the type of work it is called upon to perform, so it is logical to divide these animals into groups according to their work load. The diet of animals within each group is then broadly similar and can be better understood.

(1) *High work loads for sustained periods:* This group contains the dogs I call 'country dogs' which are hunting and pack animals: Beagles, Bassets, Fox Hounds, also gundogs, Retrievers, Pointers and Labradors. In addition, sled dogs used in polar regions should be placed in this group. They all work for sustained periods and need a high level of available energy during these prolonged periods.

(2) *High work loads for relatively short periods:* This group covers the Greyhounds and Whippets. During their normal training schedule they need little more than the normal maintenance diet, but for short periods, tremendous energy demands will be made upon them, e.g. when they are racing. Herd and cattle dogs, sheepdogs etc. also come into this group since they have low energy requirements most of the time but intermittently are called upon to use energy at a very high level when they are rounding up their charges.

(3) *Varying work loads, coupled with high stress levels:* This group covers the guide dogs and the guard dogs,

dogs that live on their nerves. They need high energy levels to cope with the stress involved in their work and in addition, have varying demands for physical activity, depending on the type of work they are doing.

Obviously, the diets for each of these groups of working dogs have to vary. Let us now examine these diets more closely.

Group 1 When working these dogs will often require up to four times as much energy food as on their rest days when food is merely required for maintenance. Temperature also affects energy requirements and since most hunting takes place in the winter, the amount of food supplied will have to be increased according to the temperature in which the hounds are working. If too much food is fed, the animals will put on weight and no fat hound is going to be a good worker. On the other hand, if insufficient food is available, the animals are going to flag when hunting and this, too, is unsatisfactory.

The timing of the meal is also important; two factors have to be considered. First, working animals can suffer from a condition known as gastric dilation or torsion. This starts with an accumulation of gas on the stomach and can lead ultimately to torsion or twisting of the stomach or bowel. This gas formation due to fermentation is more likely to occur following a large meal and strenuous exercise and so the dog should not be fed immediately before working. On the other hand, the work load within the group often increases the energy requirements fourfold and to work a dog on a completely empty stomach is obviously asking for trouble. Indeed it has been shown that hounds, particularly when working hard, will sometimes flag due to a reduction in the circulating blood sugar level, just as our blood sugar drops, (if we are to believe the adverts) if we do not have a break and our elevenses! From this it seems rational to give the animal food not less than two hours before it is due to work.

When work is finished, it is again inadvisable to give a large meal since at this time most of the blood supply will be located in the muscles which have been working hard all day. This being so, digestion is likely to be slowed down. Consequently, fermentation can more readily occur leading to gas formation and the possibility of gastric torsion or intussusception, which is the telescoping of one piece of bowel into another. A drink of water, a rest for half an hour, and then food will certainly cut down the possibility of this happening.

It is now possible to work out a rational feeding programme. On working days the quantity of food, particularly energy food has to be increased and puppy type rations of high energy, high protein are probably the most suitable for this group. Portion control or modified ad lib methods can be adopted. If portion control is practised the animal should be fed not less than two hours before it is due to work and this meal should contain a higher proportion of energy foods than the main meal, which is offered at the end of the working day, when the animal has cooled off sufficiently after the return to the kennels. This meal should be the larger meal of the day. Since there is less labour involved, most hunt kennels are today moving towards a modified ad lib method of feeding. Remember, however, that hounds and gundogs are greedy feeders and if allowed to eat their fill will very soon become obese and totally useless for any form of hunting or gun work. The amount of food required also depends on whether the animals are working or not. Therefore the self feeding method has been tailored to suit this situation.

After return to the kennels and initial cooling off, during which water is of course freely available, food is presented and the animal can help itself during the night as it pleases. Once it has emptied its bowl, that is all it will get until the next ration twenty-four hours later. This method is really a cross between portion control and ad lib feeding and can also be modified and used with success in certain pet dog situations. When working hard, should there be a possibility of flagging due to a drop in blood sugar, snacks of high energy foods should be offered and the dry and semi-moist foods or even biscuits mixed with corn oil, serve this purpose very well.

Modern scientific work has shown that a dog that is producing a high output of energy for a sustained period often has to draw on its stored fat supplies to meet its energy requirements and this it cannot do unless adequate water is available: therefore it is important that the animals have adequate supplies of drinking water during their working day. Huntsmen of the old school, of course, are convinced that gastric torsion or dilation is due solely to allowing the animal to drink too much water when it is hot. There well may be some truth in this, due to the fact that they also firmly believe that the animal should not have any water at all when it is actually working and therefore no doubt the unfortunate dog drinks far too much when it is available. This situation can be avoided if water is carried and offered to the animal frequently during the sport.

Group 2 Animals in this group sustain a high work load for only short periods. Racing Greyhounds and Whippets come into this category as do sheep or cattle dogs. The diet must provide energy during the periods of intense activity which, in the case of the Greyhound or Whippet, need only be for a few minutes two or three times a week. At the same time, the diet must not cause obesity, which in the case of the racing animal would lead to disqualification if its racing weight was exceeded by too great a margin. Feeding animals in this group can thus be a highly complicated procedure. Various racing Greyhound diets are worked out and beloved by their protagonists. All depend on providing an adequate amount of protein, minerals and vitamins together with varying amounts of energy containing carbohydrates and fats, the quantities of which will depend on whether or not the dog is racing that day. Remember also that Greyhounds, although very specialized animals, are still hounds at heart and tend to be greedy feeders. Thus, ad lib feeding is not generally practised since it can lead to obesity. Trainers usually feed their animals a minimum of twice a day, the main meal being given after the race when the dog has cooled down, with the high energy containing meal being given up to four hours before the race.

With sheep and cattle dogs, feeding is similar although not so specialized. A normal maintenance diet is perfectly adequate for most of their working day, but for short periods their energy requirements will be excessively high when they are rounding or herding their charges. Portion control feeding is usual with the main energy component in the morning feed, approximately two hours before the commencement of work and the main protein containing meal in the evening after work has finished. Since Collies and Sheepdogs are not such greedy feeders as Greyhounds, modified ad lib feeding can be practised for this meal with success. Many shepherds are fully aware of the value of snacks during the working day. Bacon fat is the usual one and is often given to a dog as a reward for doing a good job. Scientifically it would perhaps be better to give it in anticipation of a job well done.

Group 3 Police dogs, guard dogs and guide dogs have varying energy commitments depending on their work load but all these animals use energy due to the nervous stress imposed upon them by their work. Energy requirements for physical work will vary tremendously; a guide dog, for example, depends entirely for its exercise on the activity of its owner and this obviously will vary not only with the individual but also with the time of year and type of occupation. None the less, the same principles apply as to any of the working dogs: they must have high energy foods in order that they can carry out their work efficiently. Self feeding probably is more beneficial to animals in this group since they can feed themselves during their off duty periods.

Certain special factors however relate.

Office and factory guards often have to defecate in the working area and this can be unpleasant for the personnel. The aim therefore should be to provide high energy, low bulk diets in order that the quantity and frequency with which the dog defecates is reduced to a minimum. Canned food and also soft-moist diets are probably the most suitable in this respect.

How much to feed the animal can only be ascertained by day-to-day assessment of bodily condition, since work loads vary so enormously. I can recall a couple of Wolfhounds I used to keep as pets and also campaign around the shows. Due to my own workload, their exercise programme was rather variable and erratic. I found that to keep them in top condition, they would have to have three times as much food when having sufficient exercise as compared with the days when they had, of necessity, to lead more sedentary lives. When spending their time travelling long distances to shows, just lying in the back of an estate car, they would often require twice as much food as at home, on one of their sedentary days, the extra being used solely to satisfy the demands of nervous energy expended during the travelling since those dogs knew where they were going and used to get worked up about the forthcoming show. To know how much food to feed daily became a matter of close inspection of the animals' condition; no other method was as satisfactory. My feeding regimen was to use a dry diet ad lib during the night and portion control feeding of high energy containing nutrients during the day, depending on whether or not they were going to a show or there was a lot of exercise in the offing. In this way they were kept in reasonable condition.

Throughout this book I have emhasized the value of unsaturated fatty acids, e.g. cooking oil, as the best form of energy for the dog. Certain specialized types of working dogs, however, of which the sled dog is the extreme example, require specially formulated high energy diets, since the addition of cooking oil to a mainly meat diet fed to sled dogs would require very large quantities and the meat would be so diluted that the dog, in order to fulfil its energy requirements, would not obtain sufficient of the rest of the nutrients. For this reason, diets containing protein of high digestibility must be ensured.

9

The pregnant and lactating bitch

Just like dogs themselves, canine pregnancies come in all shapes and sizes, but one factor is common to them all: reproduction for the bitch is the most critical stress she can encounter. A healthy male dog can sire hundreds of puppies with virtually no stress at all but the bitch is called upon to use a tremendous amount of energy, not only while pregnant, but also while she is suckling her puppies. If her feeding is not organized to cope with these demands, she will draw upon her own body reserves, irrespective of how meagre these may be. If her standard of nutrition prior to pregnancy has not been adequate she can be in dire trouble and take many months to recover. Apart from the health of the bitch, the future health and condition of the puppies also has to be considered. Occasionally a bitch that is herself in poor condition will rear a litter of smashing offspring but generally puppies from poor bitches make poor doers.

The ideal condition of a bitch about to be mated is that of an animal that has been correctly fed and exercised from the moment of weaning. She should be neither obese nor thin, and should have good muscle tone, that is to say, she should not be flabby but should be in a good, hard condition. This condition should be maintained throughout pregnancy, for the phsyical act of whelping or parturition, involves a lot of hard work, hence its popular name, labour. An animal that is in flabby condition will have a much harder time delivering her offspring.

Over the years I have come to recognize two great groups of pregnant bitches, the deliberate pregnancies and the mistakes. Into the first group go those that are electively mated including show animals and also pet bitches that are often mated prior to being spayed. A third class includes those pet bitches that are mated 'for their own good'. In the other group are all those poor unfortunates that have 'got out' and it even includes a few whose sex the owners genuinely didn't realize until the imminent happy event!

Let us look at each of these classes more carefully.

If a bitch has had a successful show season, the natural progression is to have a litter of puppies from her. From the nutritional point of view this animal is probably in better condition than those in any of the other categories. In order to have been successful in the show ring, as outlined in the previous chapter, she must have been intelligently fed and cared for and the condition that has led to success in the show ring is not very different from that required for the successful mating, pregnancy and whelping. Here is an animal with good muscle tone, not too thin, nor carrying excess weight: in other words, an animal in tiptop condition.

When presented with a pregnant pet bitch, my stock question is always, 'Why have you had her mated?' I ask this not, as I am sure some owners imagine, because I am inherently nosy and want to pry into their affairs, but merely to get some idea of the background and standard of responsibility of the owner. Quite a number of people will reply that they want to have the bitch spayed and they have been told that she must have a litter first. Where on earth does such information come from? Certainly there is no scientific evidence that a spayed bitch is in any way improved by having a litter first. Veterinary surgeons in small animal practice usually advise that bitches are not spayed when they are too immature. The reason for this is that if they are done too young problems can arise later in life. The vulva, or external sex organs, sometimes do not develop to a proper size and can cause problems with soreness or there can be urinary incontinence or an inability to hold their urine. Some veterinary surgeons, in order to ensure a bitch is not an immature puppy when she is presented for spay, insist that the bitch should have had a season first. Does this become confused in people's minds until they think that the profession is advocating a litter and not an oestrus period? I don't know. Certainly there is little difference as far as the bitch is concerned between spaying after a season and spaying a young bitch after she has had a litter, provided of course that one does it after the puppies have been weaned and before she has her next oestrus.

I think it is good advice to suggest to owners that it is better not to let their animals have a litter unless they particularly want them to, working on the good old theory that what they haven't had they won't miss! I am aware that this would not stand up to scientific argument but the rough and ready explanation is at least understandable to most owners. On the other hand, if they want the pleasure of a litter of puppies from their family pet, there is no earthly reason why they should not have her mated. Puppies are great fun provided you know what you are in for when you embark upon the venture. It is a

D

bit like family planning. I feel strongly there should be no feeling of compulsion in people's minds that bitches must be mated if they are ultimately going to be spayed. This class of bitch is probably the next after the show bitch, as far as condition is concerned, since invariably they are young, having been mated in their first or second season and are usually fairly well nourished, although some of them, particularly the more nervous terriers or terrier crosses, often are thin and also may not have been wormed properly and consequently may have parasite problems.

The third class is that of the 'for her own good' matings. The standard is now obviously dropping. These animals can be of any age and physical condition. When, on asking my stock question about the reason for having had the bitch mated I receive the reply, 'It's for her own good', my heart sinks. Frequently these owners neither want the trouble nor expense of a litter of puppies but have been forced into the situation by pressure from neighbours and other well-meaning folk who are supposed to 'know about dogs' and have ceaselessly advised that the bitch should have puppies. Although well meant this can frequently be misguided and occasionally downright dangerous advice. I recall being presented with an immensely fat, totally ungroomed, ten-year-old 'doormat' type of dog on which I even had to undertake a clinical examination to differentiate the head from the rear. When I inquired why she was pregnant, I was told indignantly that 'it was for her own good' because she was having phantom pregnancies and 'did want puppies so'. Her well-meaning owners had spent hours walking her in the local park whilst in season in order that she could select a suitable husband. Their action had been based on the advice of a woman 'down the road' who had kept dogs for years. On examination I found that the bitch was not pregnant at all but was suffering from a serious womb infection and my feelings, while conducting an emergency operation, were that perhaps the good soul who had kept dogs for years would have been better employed directing her energies towards grooming advice, rather than things sexual!

The myth that phantom pregnancies can be cured by letting the bitch have a litter, irrespective of her age or condition, is one that is firmly implanted in the minds of many owners.

Let us look at the facts.

It is normal for the bitch to undergo the same changes, both in her womb, or uterus, and her mammary glands whether she is pregnant or not. If she is not pregnant and the changes are very severe, in other words milk is produced, and the bitch is bed making, this is pseudocyesis, or phantom pregnancy. If the bitch is mated she usually makes a superb mother but not infrequently will have an even worse phantom pregnancy after her next season and obviously can't go on having puppies every season. Many of the bitches in this class are overweight and sometimes this is a deliberate act since the caring owners have decided to have a litter of puppies, which they do want, and have the misconceived notion that they must fatten the bitch up in order that she will have sufficient strength to carry and ultimately feed their litter. Overweight bitches with flabby muscles often have protracted parturition (or labour) and it is a scientific fact that they invariably have large puppies, few in number. Obviously this adds up to a difficult time all round.

The 'pregnant mistakes' are the final group and this contains the bitches that have 'got out'. They can vary from puppies themselves to sometimes quite old dogs.

The oldest I have had to attend with her first litter was fifteen and incidentally she produced three beautiful puppies. Nutritionally this class of pregnant animal can range from the superbly fit show bitch that has erred on the streets to find a spouse, to the senile bitch that could best be described as a 'disaster area' who on examination makes one wonder how she managed to survive the physical stress of mating, let alone the ensuing pregnancy!

Perhaps I should make it clear at this stage that bitches do not undergo menopause like women. There is no 'change of life' and their childbearing capacity remains with them throughout their lives, although obviously as they get older their seasons can become more irregular and their fertility drops.

NUTRITION IN THE PLANNED PREGNANCY

If you are planning to mate your bitch, the feeding procedures really should start when the bitch is a puppy herself, then you can ensure that she is in really good condition when she is mated. Once she has reached sexual maturity, she should be kept in tiptop condition and should not be allowed to become overweight, nor should she be under-exercised. If she is overweight or at all out of condition due to lack of exercise, a vigorous programme of slimming and exercise should be embarked upon and the bitch not mated until her weight and general condition have improved. Underweight bitches should have their exercise level maintained in order that they are in good, hard physical condition, but the energy foods should be increased in order that they can put on some extra weight. If weight does not increase, veterinary advice should be sought with a view to a possible clinical examination to see if there are any digestive or parasitic problems causing the thinness.

WORMING

Attention should be paid to worming before the bitch is mated and again during pregnancy. As we have already learned, certain roundworms can pass across the placenta and infect the puppy before it is born. A regular worming programme helps to reduce this.

VACCINATION

Vaccination should also not be overlooked, particularly against distemper and hepatitis since hepatitis is known to play a part in the 'fading puppy' syndrome. Provided the bitch has a high immunity against these diseases, she will pass this on to her offspring via the colostrum or foremilk. Vaccination should be boosted just before mating so that the bitch will have a good immunity when she goes to meet the stud dog, but it can be done later during pregnancy. Vaccination procedures will vary according to the level of natural disease in the area and the advice of the local veterinary surgeon should always be followed. Parvovirus vaccination should also now be considered.

OTHER FACTORS WHICH AFFECT THE FEEDING PROGRAMME

The temperament of the bitch and probable size of the litter affect the feeding programme during pregnancy. Small breeds that whelp only one or two puppies undergo just as much stress as some of the larger breeds, particularly if one looks at it in relation to the mother's weight, compared to the weight of her offspring. The smaller breeds also have a higher energy requirement per unit weight per day, in other words, they use up more energy in just living than the larger breeds and therefore their intake of food has to be *comparatively* larger. The more active, nervous, highly strung bitch also will have a higher basic energy requirement and thus requires more food than the placid lazy bitch.

A lot of well-meaning but misconceived waffle is talked about feeding the pregnant bitch. For the first month after mating there should be no change in the diet at all. This applies basically to the first two categories outlined above; with the other two categories a different line of attack is indicated. The overweight bitch requires sometimes an increase in the protein part of the diet and certainly a reduction in the energy foods in order to trim her condition. This should only be done, however, under veterinary supervision, since problems can occur with toxaemia if this is carried too far. The thin, under-nourished bitch, on the other hand, requires protein levels to be kept the same and at the same time, high energy food must be added. Some bitches undergo a reduction in appetite as the puppies grow within them and pressure increases; space is at a premium and the bulk of the food then becomes a problem. On these occasions I resort to my old standby, the fats, and increase the oily part of the diet, adding cooking oil at the rate of about 10 per cent of the total intake. A dog receiving, say, a pound of meaty food a day can therefore have up to three tablespoons of corn oil mixed in the diet.

Remember that the main nutritional stresses for the bitch occur when she is feeding her puppies and not during pregnancy. Therefore, if she is being fed an adequate maintenance diet, there should be little need to alter this during the pregnancy. Nevertheless many authorities state that food should be increased during the last month or so of gestation (pregnancy), some even suggesting by as much as 66 per cent. My experience is that this does not work very well. It is at this stage that the bitch suffers from pressure problems due to the family within her and it becomes almost a physical impossibility to get extra nutrients into her. Often she will have difficulty in even finishing her normal maintenance meal. I endeavour to overcome the problem by feeding frequent small meals, but bitches that are used to a rigorous portion control diet often do not take kindly to an alteration in their feeding routine. At this time bitches brought up on a self feeding programme often do better, since they eat little and often as the fancy takes them. An animal with a lot of abdominal distension can, during her last two or three weeks, be encouraged to convert to a self feeding programme by being offered lots of tiny meals so that she can take food more or less at will.

The size of the bitch during the last three weeks of pregnancy is no indication of litter size. Many is the time I have been completely wrong in the estimate of the number of puppies. This is due to the tremendous variation in the amount of foetal fluids carried by different animals.

As well as offering smaller meals, another method of ensuring that adequate nutriment is taken in is to formulate a concentrated diet so that the food is supplied in less bulk than in the bitch's normal maintenance diet. This is exactly what is required during lactation when the demands on the bitch are even greater, so the logical thing to do is to gradually move the bitch on to such a diet so that the problem of nourishing her when she is suckling her puppies will be solved. Such a food is easily provided if one uses one of the good quality puppy diets on the market which can be further supplemented by our old energy standby, corn oil, if necessary.

THE LACTATING BITCH

Depending of course on the size of her litter, a lactating bitch can require up to three times as much food as before she was pregnant and in order to overcome the problems of the bulk of such a diet, only a high protein, high energy food should be offered. However, most bitches *in good condition* can suckle up to about four puppies without the need for too much increase in food during lactation, but above four the needs rise rapidly. With the toy breeds, even one or two puppies represent strain so they should be fed a high protein, high energy food from the outset.

My experience is that the majority of bitches are unable to rear more than about eight puppies without losing condition irrespective of their diet unless they receive help from the owner in the form of hand feeding, or supplementing of the puppies. This is because they are just not able to eat sufficient quantities of food to maintain themselves and their litter and they tend to give everything to their puppies with typical maternal self sacrifice. Even with the giant breeds, allowing them to attempt to rear twelve or fourteen puppies on their own invariably results in a bitch that, at weaning, is in poor condition. This will often take months to repair and, in the case of the show bitch, this can be disastrous. The puppies will also have had to work harder for the available milk supply and so the bitch will have very pendulous teats and breasts, which in certain breeds such as the Labrador Retriever and the German Shepherd, can take months to return to normal.

SUPPLEMENTS

Many owners, particularly novice breeders, seem to be obsessed with the need to supplement the bitch's diet during pregnancy with a veritable plethora of vitamins and minerals. If the bitch is receiving an adequate diet most are totally unnecessary with the possible exception of some form of vitamin D and calcium during the last two or three weeks of pregnancy and during lactation. Even the need for these is doubtful in the case of the bitch that is being fed one of the commercially formulated diets. The majority of supplements do no harm provided the makers' recommendations are followed but it should be remembered, particularly with some of the calcium preparations, that there should be a ratio between calcium and phosphorus and if this is not adhered to, problems can arise. Raw chopped liver in moderate amounts, say an ounce or two, twice a week for a thirty-pound bitch, will provide many of the minerals together with any vitamin D necessary. Eggs and fish provide useful sources of essential amino acids, while milk or milk substitutes, instead of water to drink, will provide a useful form of fluid that at the same time contains a mass of energy and nutrients. Most people do give nursing bitches milk to drink in the hope that it will stimulate more milk production, but remember if the bitch tends to be overweight a lot of milk given to her at this time will only make her put more weight on and in such a case, water is perfectly adequate.

WEANING

Once the puppies become independent of the bitch, her food should be cut down, but obviously if she is in poor condition she should be fed at a high level for much longer. If the bitch has a copious milk supply at the time the puppies are due to leave her, it can often be dramatically reduced without resort to any drugs by giving her only water to drink on the first day the puppies have left, then on the second day, giving her a quarter of her normal diet, increasing to 50 per cent on the third day, 75 per cent on the fourth day, and so on. In this way, it is surprising how rapidly her milk supply disappears. A similar regimen often works for a bitch in phantom pregnancy too!

10

The fat dog

The fat dog is an all too common sight in any veterinary surgeon's waiting room. About 75 per cent of all canine patients presented for any condition are to some extent obese, but what do we mean by obesity? What do we mean by a fat dog? Many are so overweight that visual examination is sufficient.

I well remember a nice Pembroke Corgi whose weight should have been in the range of 24 lb that actually weighed 68 lb! There was no doubt about this dog's gross state. Even the owners did not have to be convinced, but what about the others? The ones whose owners, when taxed about their dog's overweight condition, tell you that it is 'heavy boned' or that it is in 'full coat'. I am always amazed how owners will notice these physical attributes but will totally miss the fact that over the months or years their animal has been steadily, insidiously, increasing its body weight.

In man the situation is far more simple. For every height and physical type there is an optimum weight and if a person is more than 15 per cent over the recommended figure, they can be classed as obese and no one will argue. Dogs, unfortunately, come in all shapes and sizes. To complicate matters more, they are also covered with hair.

Obesity is probably simplest to define in the pedigree

dog. Every breed has an optimum weight and if you weigh a particular animal and it is more than 10–15 per cent over that weight then you can say with authority that the animal is obese. With equal authority, you can quote the breed standard and state a target weight.

What about the mongrel?

Here we have no idea what the normal or non-fat model should weigh or look like and therefore one can hardly authoritatively suggest a target weight, or even guess the percentage of excess weight being carried. This is one of those areas where in veterinary work we cannot follow too closely the pattern set by our colleagues engaged with human obesity problems. They can weigh the patient, take waist and chest measurements, measure skin thickness and compare the results with sets of tables relating to physique to determine exactly the percentage of obesity.

How then, can we determine whether or not our dog is fat or in good condition? I run my fingers across the rib cage and if I am able to count each individual rib without too much pressure and at the same time in a close coated animal (or a long coated one when it is damp after a bath) I am unable to see those ribs when the animal is at rest, I regard the dog as neither too fat nor too thin. In other words, there is some covering of fat under the skin, but not too much.

CAUSES OF OBESITY

I am always intrigued by the number of fat animals that are owned by people of like physique. Without any prompting it is frequently brought to my attention. I will comment on the dog's fatness and immediately is the reply, 'Oh dear, he is just like me, he likes his food.' Depressing in its familiarity. I often reflect that we would be indeed strange if we did not like our food but that does not necessarily mean that we have got to endure obesity and that goes for man and his pets.

Very few people are encountered with a 100 per cent obesity problem, in other words, with weight being twice the normal, without there being some underlying disease process causing the condition. In the dog, weights far in excess of 100 per cent are an everyday sight in any small animal practitioner's consulting rooms. Only a very small percentage of these animals are suffering from any form of disease process to account for their condition: the majority are suffering solely from over-indulgent owners who persist in stuffing them full of energy foods, usually biscuits, far in excess of requirements. Once the animal's weight starts to increase, its exercise tolerance decreases so that ultimately it is totally incapable of using up its excess energy intake by exercising. In this way, the over-indulgent owner has quite unwittingly set up a vicious circle since the less time the dog spends in exercise the more time it has to get under the owner's feet, worrying for food. Eating is now one of the few pleasures left to it.

Whenever I mention an animal's obesity, the almost invariable reply at the outset is, 'Oh, it's not for what he eats.' Unfortunately, it is for what he eats, for the obesity is the result of excess calorific intake in relation to energy expenditure of the animal.

Glandular causes are often cited to me by indulgent owners as an excuse for the obesity of the dog. However, the majority of these animals, apart from fatness, are quite healthy and certainly initially are prepared to run and to exercise and to behave in every way as normal. Animals with glandular disease in one form or another usually show other signs besides fatness. They are lethargic, disinclined to exercise, or else pant a lot if they do. Frequently they have skin problems which lead one to the basic nature of their condition.

Another frequently held belief is that neutering makes animals fat. If this were so, surely there would be far more fat cats around than one commonly sees since the majority of the cats seen in towns are neutered and yet very few of them are grossly obese in the way that our dogs often are. Fat cats do exist, of course, but they are small in number compared with the number of fat dogs.

I have personally kept spayed bitches for years and at present have two spayed Basset bitches, both of which are particularly greedy feeders, but neither of those bitches altered weight after being spayed. It should be remembered that when an animal is de-sexed its food conversion ratio alters and it does tend to convert food more efficiently because its energy requirements tend to fall slightly, depending on the age, temperament, and breed of the animal. However, if a close watch is kept on the situation and as soon as the animal starts to put on weight, carbo-hydrates and the fat part of the diet are restricted, fat the dog will not be, although it may be hungry. Hunger, after all, will present fewer problems to the animal than obesity ultimately does.

I am always disappointed at the number of owners who blame their dog's fat condition on its neutering, be it male or female and say they wish they had never had it done. I think this is a shame since it is, after all, the food and not the neutering that has resulted in the animal's state. Further, any veterinary surgeon will tell you that the majority of fat patients actually seen in everyday practice are entire anyway. The pet dog living exclusively indoors is a highly inactive animal. In order to alleviate its boredom, all that is left to it is to eat and consequently it tends to hang around looking for food and gradually trains its owner into believing that it needs more food! Often this is of the completely wrong type, such as titbits, sweet things, typical energy foods, which are predictably laid down to fat since the dog is not expending enough energy to use up the surplus. The fatter it gets the less its calorific output. In other words, its energy output decreases since the dog becomes less and less inclined to move, basically because its limbs are not designed to carry such weight and it becomes an effort to do so.

The giving of titbits has been discussed elsewhere in this book but must be faced squarely in the case of the fat dogs. Almost invariably when discussing the weight problem of any animal we are first told that it is 'not for what he eats'. I then inquire what he does eat and if I am to believe the diets that are usually trotted out to me, I would expect to be examining for undernourishment or starvation rather than the reverse! Frequently the owner tells me that the dog doesn't finish up its meal. I then move on to the area of titbits or treats and I suspect that many owners have feelings of guilt about these, since I invariably have the greatest difficulty in extracting honest information about the amount of extras. I do not think this is deliberate: it almost becomes a sub-conscious forgetfulness of the odd biscuit, the odd sweet that is given to the dog.

I try to suggest a positive line of action for the owner. I suggest that for twenty-four hours, everything the dog receives should be written down, both for his meals and his extras. This is a very good tip, incidentally for any one to try who thinks they have an obese dog and feels he is not eating very much. These results are sometimes quite shattering and on occasions I have worked out the calorific content of the total intake of both titbits and food and found that the extras amount to more calories than the actual meal. Is it surprising in those circumstances that the animal does not finish up its meal? Another point that I make to owners at this stage is that they should compare the total intake of their animal with their own intake over a similar period and then compare their weight with their pet's weight and think how little the animal really does need. For example a Poodle weighing 14 lb would really need only about one tenth of the total intake of a person weighing ten stone. In actual terms this is not quite correct since the dog does need slightly more, but nevertheless it is a salutary exercise to contemplate.

MANAGEMENT

As soon as the owner realizes the dog is putting on weight, he invariably flies to the remedy of increasing exercise. In the grossly obese dog, this can only do more harm than good. The joints are just not capable of sustaining this vastly increased weight and to inflict upon them the added burden of exercise is often too much for them and this is one of the reasons why operations to stabilize joints such as the knee joint are so common. Increased exercise also adds a burden to the overworked heart and respiratory system and thus instead of solving the problem, since the fat animal's exercise tolerance has dropped anyway, endeavouring to force the unfortunate pet to take more exercise will do a lot of harm.

WEIGHT REDUCTION

In order to establish successful weight reduction it is pointless to just furnish a suggested diet. Tremendous support has to be given to the owners. One has to establish rapport. Initially I weigh the animal and at the same time show the owner how to do this himself if at all possible. If the dog is not too large, the best method is to weigh yourself on the bathroom scales and then weigh yourself plus dog and subtract one from the other. I also ask the owner to return at weekly or fortnightly intervals in order to encourage him with the new regime which is being evolved and at the same time carry out frequent weight checks. It is important not to be disappointed at the small weight loss of your animal, particularly if he is being weighed every week. Provided it is going down you are on the right lines. Diet history is the next stage and this often takes a few consultations, particularly if one is to establish an accurate assessment of the titbits. If no weight loss is noted over two or three weeks, I increase the cross-examination regarding the titbits situation and it is surprising what comes to light. This is especially true of clients who did not consult you in the first place over a primary obesity problem, or who are often obese themselves and have a far greater mental block when it comes to honest diet history. I then try to work out a diet that does not result in too much hunger as far as the patient is concerned, but at the same time results in a lowered calorific intake. Unfortunately, particularly in the more obese patient, weight reduction must go hand in hand with a certain amount of hunger. One either has a satisfied dog that ultimately dies at an early age because it is off its legs, or has a heart or chest problem, or one has a healthy, albeit hungry animal.

What we have to do is to try to organize the diet so the hunger is at least bearable, otherwise the animal will be irritable and can end up no fun to live with. Merely reducing the amount of the dog's regular diet is no answer. You can get nutritional deficiencies and will only increase the animal's hunger anyway. The dog will then start searching for other sources of food and it is in this way that it can end up as an acute emergency having got into the refuse sack and eaten the chicken carcase or suchlike.

The basic object of the diet is to reduce the number of calories by replacing as much of the fat and digestible carbohydrates (or starch) with indigestible carbohydrates so that the dog is eating the same amount of food but is not receiving the same amount of calories. The protein content of the food remains the same or if anything is increased. This is the theory behind the special prescription diets that are today available. These are very convenient and highly satisfactory, but are often not very palatable although I would personally persevere much longer than the majority of owners do. A good tip if the dog is put on to one of these prescription diets is to gradually wean him on to it by mixing it with the normal diet and reducing the quantity of normal food and increasing the quantity of the special, obesity diet over a period of a week to ten days.

A palatable obesity diet can be quite easily achieved by using one of the high protein, meaty, canned foods and instead of mixing this with biscuit, using a spoonful or two of All Bran or even rabbit bran as a bulking agent. In order to ensure that the animal is not too hungry, I always suggest that the total estimated quantity is fed in divided meals throughout the day, rather than one or two main meals.

HOW MUCH TO GIVE?

This can be a problem. Ideally the diet should contain 60 per cent of the animal's energy requirements needed to maintain it at its optimum or target weight. In this way it should lose weight and in order to encourage owners, I estimate that if this 60 per cent rule is adhered to then a 20 lb dog will safely lose initially about 1 lb a week. This will tail off to less than a quarter of a pound a week as he reaches his target or optimum weight. A 40 lb dog will lose correspondingly 2 lb a week tailing off to $\frac{1}{2}$ lb in the last few weeks. My experience has been that the target weight takes on average about three months to achieve although some animals, like some people, take considerably longer.

It should be remembered that it takes about four times as long to reduce an animal's weight by a given amount as it does to increase it.

Dogs that are used to titbits can be given treats in the form of lean baked meat which can be cut into squares and baked at the bottom of the oven when something else is being cooked. These are then offered in place of the usual sweets or biscuits.

PROBLEM CASES

If the animal fails to lose any weight, careful veterinary examination should rule out any underlying cause. Careful investigation of diet and history is once more mandatory and it is surprising how often one finds that the owner's best efforts are being sabotaged either by a well-meaning member of the family or a neighbour who gives him just one little biscuit, or by the dog stealing from children in the house, or the birds' bread in the garden. . . . When the owner despairs, I have sometimes taken these animals in and put them on a total starvation diet for a few days, in order to demonstrate to the owner that it is possible for the animal to lose weight. This may sound cruel until one remembers that the dog basically is a hunter and he may go for long periods without food after a kill without losing his ability to hunt for his next meal.

The older the animal becomes, the less are its calorific requirements since less exercise is taken. The energy part of the diet should be correspondingly reduced in order to prevent the fatness of old age. The dog's joints will be becoming stiff due to old age anyway, so let us not add to his burden. Feeding the aged, just like feeding the obese, requires no magic formula, just a little common sense and a lot of perseverance on the part of the owner. The result is a long-lived, happy animal. Surely that is reward enough.

11

Thin dogs – reasons and remedies

The essential cause of obesity, irrespective of contributory factors, is the intake of too much energy food, in other words too many calories. Thinness on the other hand can have many causes, and its correction can be even more difficult than obesity.

CAUSES

(1) *Lack of Nutrients* This is *starvation*. Perhaps it is surprising that starvation still exists with our pets today, but unfortunately it does and sometimes the reasons are not altogether obvious. I remember an owner of an immensely fat Labrador who was brought in one day because she was having difficulty getting on her legs from a sitting or lying position. On examination it was very obvious that here was a desperate situation. In consequence a crash diet was devised which reduced her weight by about 20 lb in half as many weeks. This certainly prolonged her life although in the end we had to put her to sleep due to joint problems, which I am sure were exacerbated, if not actually caused, by her gross obesity. Ultimately the owners bought a Labrador puppy to replace her; they were determined that their previous errors in management should not be repeated but unfortunately this time they went too far the other way.

I inoculated the puppy and then did not see her for about six months, when she was presented one Sunday afternoon with a cut foot. I was horrified. The dog, now nine months old, barely weighed 30 lb. Every rib was visible, she was nervy and 'on edge' although on clinical examination she did not appear to be suffering from any nutritional disease. Her coat was good, her eye was bright and she was not found to have any parasites. Straightforward starvation did cross my mind, but I dismissed it in relation to these owners. On questioning, however, I learned that she was being fed half a tin of Pedigree Chum a day and nothing else. The owners were so frightened at the effect of feeding biscuits ad lib to their previous pet that they were determined they would not repeat their mistakes. Unfortunately they forgot they were now dealing with a puppy who was very much more active than its elderly predecessor and was also growing and needed a high calorie content diet in order to cope with its energy demands. I placed the dog on a sensible diet with fats and biscuits added and its weight rapidly rose to a satisfactory level, although the bitch has always remained somewhat lean and nervous, a stark reminder that feeding during the formative months of puppyhood can be crucial.

(2) *Activity* Puppies and young dogs vary in their activity levels. Some use a lot of energy and exercise themselves just running around the house. When working out a suitable diet, even for a puppy from one of the toy breeds, due allowance must be made for the energy that is dissipated in self exercise, otherwise you are likely to end up with a thin dog. Even greater provision for energy requirements must be made in the diet of the working group of dogs, as we have already seen.

(3) *Stress* This can manifest itself in many ways and

often results in a thin dog. The hyperactive, nervous terrier is a classic example. We have also discussed the effects of stress on the experienced and outwardly calm and collected show dog, who will lose weight and condition when being heavily campaigned around the shows. Some dogs are far more stress sensitive than others. It should also be remembered that animals do not always suffer from the same stresses as affect their owners. Some forms of stress are obvious and can be easily corrected by attention to diet. Examples are rapid growth, especially in the bigger breeds, pregnancy and lactation. Other forms are more difficult to elucidate and therefore more difficult to treat. Some dogs are 'environment attached' and can undergo stress when separated from their homes for any reason. This is what occurs in the giant breeds when kennelled even for a short period so that even though receiving extra food, the boarded Great Dane or Wolfhound will often go home after two weeks' holiday a shadow of its former self, with the owner convinced that the animal has been neglected while in kennels.

Loss of condition can also occur due to alteration in the family environment, for example, the arrival of a new baby, when jealousy can often make a dog lose pounds. Similarly, any disharmony in the home can have profound effects on the animal's wellbeing often without the owners realizing what is happening. This dissipation of energy can often be overcome with patience and care on the part of the owner, coupled with the addition of more energy nutrients, i.e. carbohydrates in the form of cooked starch (biscuits) and fats in the form of corn oil mixed in the food.

Stress associated with surgical or medical problems also requires dietary attention. The dog will lose weight or fail to gain weight following the illness although appearing to have recovered in every other way. In these cases, not only should the energy part of the food be adequate, but care taken to ensure that sufficient digestible protein is available. The digestibility of protein has been previously discussed and we know that some protein, for example tendons or gristle, are of low digestibility and really act as little more than bulking agents in the food, whereas other protein, for example that found in eggs, is of the type of amino acids or basic building blocks which are essential to the dog, and therefore this protein is of high digestibility as far as the dog is concerned. It is for this reason that eggs are so very often prescribed for dogs recovering from disease or any form of illness. Remember, however, that they should be cooked in order that the avidin which they contain is rendered harmless and does not destroy biotin which is one of the B vitamins and equally essential to the convalescent animal.

Convalescent animals should receive protein in the form of good quality meat or cottage cheese with cooked cereals or Farex, rice pudding or porridge supplying the carbohydrate fractions. Fats can be added in the form of our friend, cooking oil. If a home-made high energy diet is being formulated, vitamins and minerals should not be forgotten, which brings me back once more to my theme that the provision of any balanced home-made diet is a complicated undertaking. A commercial puppy diet, together with extra energy foods in the form of biscuit or the addition of corn oil will fill the bill very much more easily and probably more effectively than any home-made diet.

(4) *Illness emaciation* The cases of thinness discussed up to now will all respond to any adjustment of diet.

However, not all thin dogs can be cured by altering their food and this is where the thin dog differs from the fat, who will certainly become thinner if its food intake is reduced. Dogs that are thin because of organic disease are different. There are several conditions which prevent the dog from either digesting or absorbing the food that it eats and consequently it will fail to gain weight irrespective of how much extra food is offered. There are several conditions that fall into this category:

(a) Pancreatic insufficiency: this involves the pancreatic gland, the function of which is described in the chapter on digestion. As we will discuss more fully in the chapter on Special Diets, improper functioning of the gland results in enzymes not being produced in the correct amounts and therefore the food that the animal eats is not properly digested and absorbed and the dog suffers from undernourishment.

The condition is not a rare one.

On clinical examination the animal is usually thin and even emaciated. It often has a ravenous appetite and passes copious, evil smelling faeces. Although there is often a lot of gas in the bowel it does not necessarily always have diarrhoea.

(b) Worms: in the growing dog, a high worm burden, particularly of roundworms, can cause leanness. Remember that young dogs of the small or toy breeds can also suffer from severe tapeworm infestation which also can result in a ravenous appetite and lack of body weight. Larger breeds although equally infested, do not appear to suffer such ill effects.

(c) Malabsorption syndrome: this is another common cause of thinness in certain breeds. The dog usually has diarrhoea and is fairly thin and often has a pot-bellied appearance similar to a wormy animal. Bowel sounds are often audible. Flatus or wind is frequently present. This condition can be due to several causes:

(i) Types of gastro enteritis.

(ii) Villus atrophy which is foreshortening of the little finger-like processes or villi which occur in the small intestine in order to increase the absorption area actually in contact with the digested food (see Figure 4). Obviously if the villi are shortened for any reason, contact area is reduced and less food is capable of being absorbed in any particular period.

(iii) Lack of absorption of digested foods into the lymph system via the lacteals which are found in the villi.

These are only some of the problems of malabsorption.

All the causes of thinness in this category need careful diagnosis before treatment. Some will respond to diet but other forms of treatment may be necessary. Therefore it is even more worthwhile visiting your veterinary surgeon if you have a thin dog, since without expert advice, many cases will not respond to just feeding extra rations. The aim of this book is certainly not to act as a Do It Yourself manual, but merely to throw some light on the complex problem of canine nutrition in a down-to-earth fashion. Many pitfalls exist in attempting to diagnose and treat either thinness or fatness without expert help.

I recall the owner of a Whippet worried about his dog's thinness. On clinical examination I found the dog in superb bodily condition. The owner had never owned a Whippet before and was ignorant of normality in the breed. On the other hand I can also remember being consulted by an elderly lady who was concerned that her dog was getting fat and was quite convinced that it was because both she and her pet were ageing and less able to take exercise. On examination I found the dog to be totally emaciated but with an enlarged fluid filled abdomen suggestive of chronic heart failure. Just beware! Pitfalls are many.

12

The fussy, faddy feeders

For as long as I can remember, I have shared my home with dogs. They have usually been in quantity and of widely differing breeds but never have I owned, or been associated with a fussy, faddy or difficult feeder! In practice, however, I am not infrequently consulted by worried owners who assure me that their dogs are difficult to feed. I became intrigued and on further investigation, found that the cases fell into two distinct groups. I use the word case rather than animal, since as I think will become apparent, some of the problems may be owner induced rather than due to the dog. My two classes are 'normal' animals and 'nervous' animals.

FUSSY FEEDERS THAT LOOK NORMAL

These animals never appear in any way underweight and on veterinary examination usually appear in the pink of condition. Owners of these animals seem always concerned, however, that they are very fussy or faddy with their diets. This may well be due to the owner's inexperience. Consider the diversity in the sizes of our pet dogs. I have owned a Chihuahua weighing $3\frac{1}{2}$ lb, alongside an Irish Wolfhound weighing 122 lb. It takes a lot of expertise to be able to ascertain accurately the correct amount of food to feed on a day-to-day basis to each of these widely differing animals. Without the experience, owners grossly overestimate the needs of their pets since the only base line they have is their own daily intake of food. The majority of dogs gratefully accept that which is offered and no problem exists in the owner's minds until the dog's fatness precipitates other problems, and that, as we have seen, warrants a chapter to itself.

It should be remembered that some dogs are not greedy feeders and will control their own calorific intake, eating only as much as they need. If their needs have been overestimated by their owners, such an animal will then appear as a fussy, faddy or difficult feeder, since it will sometimes not touch the food at all if it does not feel hungry that day. When I tell owners this, invariably they will say, 'Ah, yes, but if I coax him and hand-feed him, he will eat.' The dog is then not eating through hunger, but merely to please the family! Some owners adopt a different approach and promptly replace the food offered with something else and it is indeed a strong-willed animal that does not ultimately succumb to one of the delicacies offered. This animal's owner's complaint is then that they are 'fed up with the expense of trying to feed the dog', since they have to keep buying different foods.

The reason I have never had a difficult feeder is because I would neither resort to hand-feeding, nor would I ever dream of offering another type of food. My dogs just have to go without until the next day. The only exception is in the case of illness or convalescence where the extra attention and fuss does much to aid recovery.

Dogs are not people; they have a completely different digestive process and a completely different metabolism. Research has shown that dogs can undergo total starvation very much better than people and this is related to their original lifestyle. A dog had to hunt for its food, it then killed its prey and would gorge itself until satisfied. Afterwards it would rest until it felt hungry enough to hunt for its next meal. Sometimes, if the hunting proved unsuccessful, the dog would have to undergo total starvation for perhaps days on end, but at the same time, to retain enough strength to continue hunting for its next meal.

Total starvation in man leads to all sorts of problems due to the breakdown products of body tissues building up in the bloodstream and affecting the liver and other organs. In addition, the blood sugar level drops and the person feels weak and extremely ill. In contrast, the dog undergoing starvation appears to retain all his faculties and furthermore, his blood sugar level remains fairly constant so that he can still run and catch his prey with as much facility as when fully fed.

The pet dog has come a long way from the days of his wild, prey-catching ancestors, but his metabolism has not changed very much. Therefore there is no harm done if the dog goes without food for a day or two, provided he shows no other signs such as diarrhoea or sickness, or an increase in thirst, or being unduly quiet. If he appears to be normal in all other ways, there is absolutely *no need to keep offering titbits in the hope of tempting his appetite*. Make sure he has plenty of clean drinking water freely available and leave him alone.

It should also be remembered that dogs that normally drink milk or tea with sugar or other energy-containing beverages are not totally lacking in nutrients when they do not eat. Sometimes dogs, like their owners, will feel a little off colour and go without food for this reason, just as we do and often recover the next day without any form of medical attention at all. Reflect how we would feel if we were a little queasy, perhaps the result of a hangover, and we were being constantly plied with food and titbits by the family.

How long should one wait when the dog is not eating before doing something? This depends on several factors. If you feed the animal only once a day, make it wait until the next day. If on the other hand you feed twice a day, offer the next meal at the usual time. You will notice I am dwelling entirely on portion control feeding. Faddy feeders cannot exist with ad lib feeding, because they have been brought up on it and live and thrive on it; they are used to it and certainly will not be fussy about it. Observe the dog's drinking habits, make sure it is drinking and if this is within the normal range, don't worry for a few days. If possible weigh the dog. If there is no weight loss despite the reduced intake over a period of, say, five days, do not worry; then if after five to seven days the dog is still not eating properly and is now beginning to lose weight visit your veterinary surgeon.

So-called 'false' or phantom pregnancies in the bitch will often make them reduce their intake of food dramatically. Seldom do these animals appear to lose weight although the condition may continue for weeks on end. The same general rule should apply. Do not fuss. Attention will only make matters worse.

If milk production is the main problem, one of the best ways of reducing this is to withold both fluids and food for twenty-four to thirty-six hours. Pampering her will only make matters worse.

THE FUSSY FEEDER THAT IS NERVOUS

On examination dogs in this group do at least look as though they have something wrong with them. They are often lean to thin, they are usually highly strung, very

nervous animals. Many German Shepherds fall into this
category as well as smaller, short-haired terrier crosses.
Temperament is the main problem here but contributory
causes I will discuss under three headings:

(1) *Imbalanced or unpalatable diet* Often on questioning
owners, I find diets are being offered that are not entirely
satisfactory. I remember a Toy Poodle, a breed incidentally known for its faddy habits, that lived in a
household of cats. The cats liked fish and it transpired
after questioning that the dog was fed largely a fish diet
mixed with brown bread. Once a week the owner
conceded to buy the dog liver or mince and on those
days she said the dog ate quite well but pointed out that
she could not feed liver every day because 'it had a
delicate stomach' and the liver gave it diarrhoea. Anyway
she had been told by a previous veterinary surgeon to
keep it on a white meat diet, i.e. fish. I ventured to suggest
that perhaps the dog did not like fish particularly, meat
after all is the most palatable protein food for a dog. I
suggested to the owner to try mixing fish and meat
together to see if that would control the diarrhoea. This
apparently solved the problem and two months later the
animal was up to normal weight and there was no longer
any history of it being fussy over meals.

(2) *Wrong environment* Some nervous animals make
excellent children's pets and are happy to play and romp
with the family but prefer to feed in isolation. If such a
dog is fed in the living room, as often happens, with the
television at full blast and the kids squabbling, the poor
dog will rush to its food, gobble down two mouthfuls,
belch violently and then retire into a corner to enjoy its
flatulence in whatever form of solitude it can achieve
amid the hubbub! When the fully fed family finally
realize that the dog has not eaten its dinner, they will often

take it into its corner and hand-feed the dog and the animal will respond by eating readily. Here the difficulty is due entirely to the animal's highly strung temperament, coupled with a lack of appreciation of its needs by the otherwise caring and well-meaning family. Once the owners realize the needs of the dog, matters can be quickly put right. Just give it somewhere quiet to eat its meal.

(3) *Special cases* These include those nervous animals that have been subject to extra stress. Animals recovering from debilitating illness, or those that have undergone a change in environment or ownership, are the cases that come readily to mind. A bit of patience and TLC (Tender Loving Care) is all that is needed. Here is a group of animals that do need pandering to, hand-feeding and fussing. They are part of the everyday work of a veterinary hospital. Frequently, when animals are ill and removed from their environment and their owners, they will not eat and it is for this reason that time spent finding out from the owner the special likes and dislikes of the particular pet is of immense value.

Similarly if you have recently taken on an adult animal and find he is difficult over his food, it is worth while, particularly if he is of nervous temperament, to try to find out exactly what his old owners fed him and also where and when. If the dog is used to being fed in the living room in the evening try to continue to do this and you will find that he will settle in much more easily and quickly.

E

13

Special diets

Anyone who has had an old dog with kidney problems, or alternatively a dog with recurrent diarrhoea, will realize that diet plays a very important part in the management and treatment of many diseases. In this chapter I will endeavour to try to explain the basis of some of the more common special diets and their value to the animal. Mention has been made of bland diets from time to time in this book and I am sure we have all at times had occasion to feed our dogs such a diet. 'Bland' means 'smooth' but to many people this means milky foods, creamed to a smooth consistency. In its strict medical context, bland does not entirely mean this. Commercial convalescent diets, which will be discussed later in the chapter, are a good example of a bland diet. Its residues are low because all the contents are of high digestibility and it is designed to be readily acceptable to the upset digestive system. Therefore it is equally suitable for an animal recovering from any sort of medical or surgical problem and none of its constituents are likely to cause any upset to a delicate digestion. This is a true 'bland' diet. However, the majority of home-made bland diets do consist of white meat or fish and milky products. From the theory we have learned earlier it will now be obvious such foods contain proteins, carbohydrates and fats of *high biological value*. In other words they contain individual nutrients that are highly digestible and contain low residues.

The incorporation of milk and milk products in bland diets should only be done with caution since, as I have already explained, some dogs are not capable of digesting milk and in these cases diarrhoea problems are more likely to be exacerbated than cured if milk is added to the diet.

HOME-MADE SPECIAL DIETS

Today as we will see, there are some excellent commercial special diets but palatability is often a problem with these and recourse often has to be made to home-made special diets. Probably the most common of these is the special diet for chronic kidney conditions. The veterinary surgeon will tell you to feed the animal on a white meat diet since the white meat protein has, broadly, a higher biological value, in other words, it yields more essential amino acids and less protein waste products than red meat and so the kidneys have less work to do in trying to excrete the non-essential part of the protein which has been broken down.

Eggs and cheese are highly digestible and very nutritious and can be added to the nephritic diet, as can milky preparations. Provided the animal is not diabetic it is often sensible to increase the carbohydrate fraction of the diet with some easily digestible form such as sugar or glucose. The aim is to try to prevent the animal having to metabolize or break down some of its own proteins for energy needs and in this way we are helping again to protect the kidneys from extra work. Another old-fashioned although very valuable tip is to give the dog barley water rather than ordinary water to drink. The reason for this is that animals with kidney problems are usually polydipsic, that is, they have a tremendous thirst. If they are allowed to drink their fill, they drink so much water that this precludes eating very much, solely due to the lack of space. Barley water will probably satisfy the dog more than drinking plain water, since it is very soothing and the dog will tend to drink less; it also contains a lot of carbohydrates which act as a useful energy source and protect the dog's kidneys from the results of further protein breakdown. It can be prepared by cooking pearl barley, thus breaking down the starch and extracting it into the fluid. This is then diluted sufficiently to be acceptable to the animal. A good tip is to flavour it with a little sugar, which often makes it more palatable when offered initially. Gradually the concentration of the barley water can be increased as the dog becomes more used to it. Robinsons Patent Barley, which is pre-cooked ground barley, can be used as an alternative to cooking pearl barley if rapid preparation is required. Dilute it similarly. Do remember that lemon barley preparations are not what is meant at all when the veterinary surgeon advises offering barley water!

Another special diet, familiar to those of us who have had dealings with puppies, is simulated bitches' milk. In the chapter on hand-rearing and weaning I mentioned some of the home-made formulae that are popular among breeders and these are, after all, special diets. These formulae are much more conveniently and probably more satisfactorily coped with by the commercial foods that are now available. As far as simulated bitches' milk is concerned, the most widely available in the UK is Lactol. It is a complete food intended for very young puppies, which is not canned, but is in dried form which has to be reconstituted with water. Provided it is made up according to directions, it is very satisfactory. Recently other products have become available which perhaps are more suitable for rearing very weak puppies. Some of these, for example Welpi, marketed by Hoechst, are available only through your veterinary surgeon.

Special canned diets and soft-moist diets are now commercially available. Of these, the most commonly used are Pedigree Petfoods products, obesity, nephritis and convalescent diets. They are all available on veterinary prescription only. It is interesting that since these diets are intended to be fed alone, they are really the only complete canned foods manufactured by this company today, since all their other canned foods are designed to be fed with the addition of some form of carbohydrates, usually in the form of biscuit. The reason for this of course is that there are cheaper and more convenient ways to pack carbohydrates than incorporating them into a can as a complete food unless a particularly special formulation is required, as obviously is necessary in the case of Petfoods prescription diets.

This brings me to the second point about special diets. Pedigree Petfoods special diets and those of some other manufacturers are available only via the veterinary profession, in other words, on prescription. Owners often ask me why this is so? After all they can buy diabetic foods, baby foods and invalid foods which are on free sale from the chemist without a prescription so why should they then have to go to the veterinary surgeon for their dog's nephritis diet? Another argument put to me is that since most of the special diets are more expensive than commercial dog food, it would hardly be bought unless there was a need. This is true, but who generates the need? The manufacturers, quite correctly, feel that the advice to purchase a special diet should emanate from the veterinary surgeon. Would any danger result from the indiscriminate feeding of special diets if this were not so? Yes, I think it would. Let us look at one or two examples:

Obesity diet is excellent for obese dogs but should this be on free sale and an owner decide to feed what he considers to be his fat bitch on obesity diet, when in fact she is pregnant, problems could occur since a low energy diet with high fibre content would be the last thing on which the pregnant bitch should be fed. Nephritis diet is ideal for the dog with defective kidney function, but is the last thing that should be fed to a growing puppy. Should the growing puppy suddenly develop a thirst, one can foresee a situation where an owner, thinking that there was some kidney problem, and wishing to do the best for his pet, promptly started offering it nephritis diet.

It is to avoid such situations that these products are on prescription.

Let us now look at the most commonly available prescription diets individually.

OBESITY DIET

This is a restricted calorie food, specially formulated for overweight dogs. Bulk is provided in the form of bran fibre and vitamins and minerals are added to ensure that the diet is a complete food for the animal. Nothing else should be fed when obesity diet is being fed to the dog. Failure of the animal to lose weight can often be traced to the owner's attempt to add a little flavour to the diet with the odd titbit, or by lacing the food with some meat, because it 'doesn't look too appetizing'. Palatability is always a problem with these special diets and if you find the animal will not touch obesity diet, even after a few days, it is probably better to switch to the feeding of one of the high protein, low bulk foods such as Pedigree

Chum adding further bulk in the form of All Bran or even rabbit bran, but avoiding increasing the carbohydrate. In other words no biscuit!

NEPHRITIS DIET

This is another complete, balanced food and nothing else should be fed. It is formulated for use in the management of chronic kidney problems in the dog.

As explained earlier, body protein can be, and is, under certain circumstances used for energy requirements, but then a lot of by-products have to be eliminated by the kidneys. If for any reason they cannot do their job the protein breakdown products accumulate in the body and the animal is said to be suffering from uraemia. This situation can also arise in a normal high protein diet, particularly if some of the proteins are not of high quality. In other words, breakdown products can accumulate. In nephritis diet, only high quality protein is used which will provide the animal with the essential amino acids necessary for tissue repair, but result in the least number of by-products. In other words there is no excess protein. This is combined with balanced fat and carbohydrate contents so that the animal has sufficient energy sources without resorting to tissue protein breakdown. One of the signs of chronic kidney disease is an increased thirst and the passing of large quantities of fluid, in other words the body's method of trying to get rid of the breakdown products. This can result in the depletion of some of the body's water soluble vitamins so these too are supplemented in the diet.

CONVALESCENT DIET

This, as previously mentioned, is a highly concentrated food which is easily digestible. It can be used for dogs and cats recovering from illnesses and also those suffering from chronic diarrhoea. It contains a high proportion of fat and carbohydrate as energy sources, together with all the necessary supplements, and is designed to provide a good quality food for those animals whose appetite may be poor.

My own experience of all these diets is that theoretically they are marvellous but since their palatability for many animals is low, getting individuals to eat the food, which after all may be foreign to their taste, is sometimes a difficult job. This I find especially so in the case of convalescent diet, where the animal's appetite often is poor to start with.

While discussing Pedigree Petfoods' special diets, I would like to mention Pedigree Chum puppy food. This is a high grade canned food which has been specially formulated for puppies and is to my mind a special diet. It is widely available and no prescription is necessary of course. Unlike the previously discussed prescription diets, its meaty flavour makes it particularly attractive to puppies and I have used it many times for weaning litters. It can be used either on its own or mixed with biscuits to supply extra energy. It contains good quality protein of high biological value, in other words, highly digestible and supplying all the essential amino acids necessary to the puppy to ensure optimum growth. It also contains ground bonemeal and whole dried milk together with all the necessary vitamins and minerals. Similar to convalescent diet it has a high fat content which is the concentrated energy source. On a dry weight basis, the fat content is actually about 10 per cent higher than ordinary Pedigree Chum, while the carbohydrate level is also higher, and at the same time the protein is not sacrificed. Apart from being ideal for the growing dog, where the requirement of nutrients and energy is almost double that needed to maintain the adult, it is also very useful for the lactating bitch and can also be used as an appetite stimulant for the convalescent animal.

These are the most common special diets, but of course there are others.

LOW SODIUM DIETS

These are useful for congestive heart failure. They can be obtained commercially or specially prepared, making sure that the salt content is kept as low as possible. The reason is that in many cardiac conditions there is kidney involvement and sodium is not excreted and therefore accumulates in the body, which in turn causes more water to be retained and so the animal rapidly develops congestive heart failure and becomes 'waterlogged'. By restricting sodium intake in the food, the condition can be controlled and water retention reduced.

ANTI-ALLERGIC DIETS

On the Continent and in America commercial diets that are hypo-allergic, in other words, not responsible for food allergies, are very popular.

If you have a dog that suffers from food allergies, a very satisfactory, low allergy producing diet can easily be produced from lamb cooked with rice. To increase the energy content, corn oil can be added. It is also worth while adding some calcium to offset the high phosphorus content of the lamb, since all meat is very low in calcium and high in phosphorus as we have seen previously.

BOOTS SPAN DIET

Ageing is a slow, progressive process which presents certain dietary problems. A special diet could well overcome some of these:

(1) Many older dogs suffer from kidney disease and consequently need a low protein diet.

(2) They have difficulty with fat digestion and since their calorific requirements are reduced as they get older, a low fat diet is indicated.

(3) They frequently drink a lot and consequently pass a lot of urine and therefore a diet with added water soluble vitamins, mainly of the B complex, would be an advantage.

(4) As the dog gradually loses its teeth with age, 'hard tack' in the form of biscuits is difficult to cope with, but in order to maintain the skeleton, calcium needs tend to increase with age so the diet must be rich in calcium.

Recently just such a food has become available as one of the Boots Span range of diets. These are canned foods, marketed by Boots to cover all the changing nutritional needs of the dog from puppyhood through to old age. Span 4 is an easily digestible diet for dogs from about seven years of age onwards. It is designed to provide sufficient proteins, carbohydrates, fats, vitamins and minerals without taxing the ageing liver and kidneys.

Other products in the Span range are puppy foods, a working dog food and basically an obesity diet. All are on unrestricted sale and are now known as 'S' Diets.

14

Feeding the sick and convalescent animal

Feeding the convalescent animal was briefly touched upon in the preceding chapter, but this is only a very small part of the general subject of feeding the dog during illness and recovery. It should be remembered that there are many conditions that can be improved by the intelligent manipulation of the animal's food and these are not only diseases caused by diet.

(*1*) *Vomiting* This is a very common condition with a multiplicity of causes. Certain signs are always present. The vomiting dog will be dehydrating and therefore polydipsic, in other words he will have a tremendous thirst and will want to drink water all the time. If this is allowed, as soon as the cold water hits the inflamed stomach lining, the stomach revolts and the dog vomits again and so loses more fluid and thus becomes more dehydrated. This in turn creates more thirst and so a vicious circle is soon established. The first action is to take up the water bowl so that the dog cannot drink any more. This simple action will by itself cut down the vomiting. It does nothing, however, to solve the dehydration problem. The animals needs fluid, it also needs energy. This can be provided as a first aid measure by making up a mixture containing the white of an egg, half a cup of water and a teaspoonful of sugar. This should be fed to the animal in small quantities. If he vomits after taking it, wait half an hour and then offer half the quantity previously given, even if it is only a teaspoonful. Albumen, or the white of egg, is demulcent, soothing the inflamed gastric lining and it also contains many essential amino acids. In addition the sugar provides some calories and the water helps to overcome the dehydration.

Thus by the very simple expedient of not allowing the animal to drink its fill and substituting controlled amounts of a very easily available fluid mixture, the dog's vomiting has been helped and at the same time, the animal is being hydrated and nourished.

(2) *Diarrhoea* This is a clinical sign of some intestinal disorder. While the basic cause is being investigated, the condition can often be improved and sometimes cured by careful attention to diet.

The bowel is inflamed and easily digestible, non-irritant food is necessary. Convalescent diet, as discussed in the previous chapter, is marvellous provided the dog will eat it. The criteria are that food residues should be low so that the inflamed bowel has less work to do. Therefore a low fibre diet with protein of high digestibility is indicated. If the animal is disinclined to eat convalescent diet, cottage cheese, eggs, fish or a suitable mixture of these will often fill the bill. Milk is excellent provided the dog can digest it. If not, then the milk will only make the diarrhoea worse.

Chronic diarrhoea results in the loss of a lot of minerals, particularly potassium and also sodium if vomiting is also present. It is therefore sensible to add a vitamin mineral supplement to the diet, especially if the condition has been present for some time.

(3) Anaemia Anaemia is a lack of blood, either red corpuscles or their contained haemoglobin. The dog can manufacture red blood cells at six times the normal rate if anaemia exists. It is therefore obvious that the right sort of nutrients should be provided if this is to occur. Food of high digestibility with protein of high biological value, in other words, highly nutritious foods, are essential. Vitamins of the B complex are required in higher levels than normal together with certain minerals, particularly iron, cobalt and copper. These can be provided using one of the mineral vitamin supplements containing trace elements and the necessary protein supplied in cottage cheese, cooked eggs, together with liver or good quality muscle meat.

(4) Fevers When an animal has a fever, its temperature is raised and hence its metabolic rate also goes up and so it uses more energy. The old adage 'feed a cold and starve a fever' is just nonsense. Admittedly many animals will not eat when their temperature is elevated but a diet of high calorific value, in other words, high in carbohydrates and fat, with sufficient digestible protein to make good breakdown losses that have occurred in the tissues due to the illness, should be provided. If the animal is disinclined to eat, often it is possible to provide highly nutritious fluids. Baby foods, Complan, Brands Essence, chicken broth, are all useful. Fluids are also essential since while not eating the animal will be burning some of the stored fat and proteins to supply energy and as we have seen previously, water is essential for this process to take place.

(5) Flatulence Putrefaction and bacterial fermentation of food in the stomach leads to gas formation which is

the primary cause of flatulence. Aerophagia, or the swallowing of large quantities of air can also cause this unpleasant condition. Breeds such as Boxers and Dachshunds, together with some of the giant breeds, seem particularly prone, especially as they get older. Eructation, or belching of wind, can produce unpleasant breath odours while that passed at the other end, sometimes with sound accompaniments, tends to be even more embarrassing. If raw meat is fed, putrefaction is more likely to occur and therefore in animals prone to flatulence, lightly cooking the meat does help. The exclusion of plant protein can also do much to help the condition, especially potatoes, beans and onions.

Control depends on maintaining the status quo of the bowel in order that the number of putrefactive bacteria present does not increase. Therefore if you happen to have a flatulent Boxer, don't try changing his diet too often just because the neighbours have said they have tried a new food which suits their dog and is marvellous. The chances are you will upset the stability of the bowel and the bugs will multiply and you will have more wind.

High protein diets should be avoided, particularly the types composed of offal which are rich in blood, since these lend themselves to very rapid putrefaction. Another tip is to reduce the quantity of food offered and increase the frequency of feeding since if less protein is available to undergo putrefaction and fermentation at any one time, there will be less gas production.

(6) *Skin diseases* Diet is very important in many forms of skin disease. In the previous chapter we mentioned anti-allergic or hypo-allergenic diets, but remember that not all skin problems are due to allergies: some can be caused by a lack of certain nutrients.

Protein deficient diets can result in poor hair growth and this condition can be seen in puppies with a high worm burden. Although they are receiving sufficient protein in their diet, they are not able to absorb sufficient due to the worms.

Itching, or pruritis, occurs with diets that are deficient in certain fatty acids. In an earlier chapter we discussed the role that the fatty acid, linoleic acid, plays in the maintenance of the healthy skin. This occurs in soya beans, corn oil and peanut oil and it is for this reason that these products are often incorporated in commercial dog food.

(7) *Coprophagia* This is more a habit than a disease. The dog eats his own and others' motions. As already mentioned, ad lib feeding is supposed to cut down or cure this unfortunate condition, the theory being that since food is available all the time the dog will eat that rather than its own stools. Many other methods have been suggested for the control of this unfortunate and unpleasant condition.

The simplest or most common is to put pepper or mustard on any stools that are passed and leave them lying around. I once tried this with a Wolfhound puppy with the habit and all she did was to develop a taste for mustard, followed by cayenne pepper and salt but she certainly did not stop eating her own motions and anyone elses that she could lay into for that matter!

A recent theory is that the condition is due to an insufficiency of some of the digestive enzymes. Enzymes only act as chemical catalysts to aid digestion and are not altered in any way as they pass through the bowel. They are therefore present in the stool when it is voided and the theory is that animals with a minimal deficiency of some of the enzymes will eat their own and other dogs' stools in order to increase the amount of available digestive enzymes in their bowel in order that their own digestion can proceed more efficiently. This is not unlike the process that takes place naturally in rabbits who eat their nocturnal droppings, which are soft, in order to increase their total vitamin B intake. It is postulated that animals can therefore be improved, if not cured, by adding meat tenderizer to their diet, since this is, in essence, a mixture of enzymes which cause the breakdown of meat protein. Since this can do no harm, even if it does no good, I certainly think it is worth a try.

(8) *Pancreatic disease* Up to now, I have discussed a variety of general conditions that can be helped by attention to the animal's diet, but let us now look at two specific diseases which respond very well to dietary control. In the dog pancreatic disease can take broadly one of two forms, (a) diabetes mellitus (sugar diabetes) and (b) pancreatic insufficiency. This is due to the make up of the pancreas. Basically there are two sorts of secreting cells.

(i) The Islets of Langerhans secrete insulin which after absorption into the bloodstream controls glucose take-up by the cells of the body. A deficiency of insulin results in diabetes. These cells constitute the endocrine portion of the pancreas.

(ii) Digestive enzymes are secreted by cells of the exocrine portion and they are involved in the digestion of protein, fats and carbohydrates. These enzymes are introduced into the duodenum via the pancreatic ducts and a deficiency in any will result in pancreatic insufficiency. Now let us consider each condition in turn.

(a) *Diabetes mellitus (sugar diabetes)* Unfortunately in the dog, unlike man, this condition can seldom be managed by diet alone and usually this has to be combined with insulin therapy. Due to the lack of secretion of insulin the body cells are unable to utilize glucose circulating in the blood and therefore the blood sugar level rises. The liver acting as the 'chemical factory' of the body, attempts to stabilize the situation and converts some of the glucose into fats. At the same time body cells are being deprived of energy and to overcome this the body starts to break down some of its protein and use this as an energy supply. We know protein is not an efficient source of energy and the products of the breakdown tend also to rise in the bloodstream and these in turn make the animal even more ill. The signs of the disease are an increase in thirst, a voracious appetite and usually a fat animal that suddenly starts to lose weight. The condition can be diagnosed relatively easily by simple urine and blood tests and with a combination of insulin therapy and careful attention to diet, dogs can be stabilized for long periods.

One of the longest living diabetics I have had as a patient lasted for seven years after diagnosis of the condition and finally died of old age at fifteen years. A standard diet must be fed each day in order that blood glucose levels can be controlled as far as possible. The dog should not have widely varying amounts of exercise from day to day; in other words, existence should be uniform with as little daily variation as possible.

Until very recently it was considered that the ideal diet for a diabetic should contain no carbohydrates but this is not absolutely necessary. Starches and other carbohydrates can be given, provided that they are in reasonable amounts. Therefore there is no need to deprive the dog entirely of biscuits or meal. However, the amount of carbohydrate should not vary from day to day, otherwise widely varying urine sugar values will be obtained and it will be difficult to estimate insulin requirements. The basic requirement is a high protein, high fat diet and this is easily supplied in the form of commercial puppy food. Some diabetic dogs, even when they appear otherwise stabilized, frequently have a voracious appetite and continue to lose weight. Under these circumstances the amount of daily food must be increased and concomitantly the amount of insulin given each day will also rise, but your veterinary surgeon will advise you on these points. Rather than increase the carbohydrates in the diet, it is sensible to increase the fats being offered, as far as possible.

(b) *Pancreatic insufficiency* This, like diabetes, tends to be a condition of stress and appears more common in nervous animals kept in urban and suburban surroundings. These dogs are subjected to much more stress than their rural counterparts. Certain breeds appear to be particularly prone to pancreatic insufficiency; among these are the German Shepherd and the Irish Setter.

The first signs are increased appetite, coupled with a nervous animal which passes large quantities of soft, often evil smelling faeces. Sometimes, normal motions are passed but they often appear to be large in quantity and light in colour. Diagnosis involves a simple test on a sample of the dog's stool. Treatment, as for diabetes, involves replacement therapy, that is supplying the enzymes that are not being manufactured by the cells in the gland, but in this case these enzymes can be supplied by mouth, since they are not digested in the same way as insulin is, if not given by injection.

Diet should be easily digestible with low fat and low fibre content. Commercial convalescent diet is useful for this purpose, provided the animal will eat it. If not, a suitable home-made substitute has to be formulated by cooking butcher's meat, allowing it to cool and skimming off the fat. This can then be offered with a small quantity of good quality biscuit. Raw pancreas in the form of sweetbreads can be fed at the rate of about half an ounce mixed with each meal. Feeding smaller meals often also is of value, particularly in those animals that only have a mild pancreatic insufficiency. More severe cases require the addition of pancreatic enzymes mixed in with the food and again the need to feed a stable, unchanging diet cannot be overemphasized.

Finally, when feeding the sick or convalescent animal, I would emphasize the value of TLC (Tender Loving Care). Small quantities of food should be offered frequently. In this way the chances are the dog will eat it at once in the fear that some other animal will appear and take it away, whereas if a large quantity is offered, the dog, feeling unwell, will probably go back to sleep thinking there is plenty and no need to worry. Another tip is to warm the food slightly to about blood heat, which will often make it smell more strongly and this will tempt the animal. A little bit of love and attention in the form of hand-feeding will often work miracles.

15

And now we know...

In the foregoing chapters of this book we have looked at various aspects of feeding. One or two points still remain to be covered.

WATER

Adequate supplies of water should always be available, not only for the dog undergoing strenuous exercise, or for animals on a self feeding, dry diet, but for every dog. Remember that the fat, pampered pet put on a strict diet in order to reduce its life threatening weight as rapidly as possible, will lose more weight if water is available in order to allow its body chemistry to turn its excessive fat into available energy.

BOWLS AND DISHES

The containers into which the food is put are also important. Many materials are used in the manufacture of dog bowls and dishes, ranging from stainless steel, aluminium, enamel ware to plastic materials and also disposable containers, both for food and drink. These latter can be made from specially coated paper products or thin plastic materials.

The softer polypropylene plastic containers are useful in that they do not make a noise when they are shuffled around the kitchen floor by greedy puppies, but have some inherent dangers since they are chewable. Some types of plastic appear to be toxic once eaten by the dog and unfortunately they do not show up on X-ray, thus if the dog is presented to the veterinary surgeon with signs of obstruction or sometimes poisoning, diagnosis can be difficult. The same problem arises with some of the very popular plastic toys as well, particularly those soft children's toys that are much beloved by the smaller puppies.

Disposable food containers are labour saving and hygienic but do tend to get eaten by the greedy feeder along with the food. The hard plastic types are less likely to be chewed but tend to crack and splinter if dropped or handled roughly, either by the dog or the owner.

I favour stainless steel as the best material for dog bowls and dishes but one disadvantage is that it is difficult to obtain non-tip vessels in this material. These are readily available in spun aluminium but this metal is sufficiently soft to allow the dog to chew and destroy the dish in a short time.

We are now at the end of the story of How To Feed Your Dog, the end of the book and as far as the dog is concerned are left only with the waste products, the stools, motions, or faeces.

At present there is a very strong anti-dog lobby in this country, and indeed, some local authorities are actively banning dogs from parks and other public places. Great play is made by the anti-dog faction on the health hazards due to worms and other diseases carried by dogs. Unfortunately, I think this move has come about due to the irresponsibility of dog owners who allow their animals to defecate in highly unsociable places. With a little time, patience and training the dog will learn to defecate where the owner wishes.

Despite all that has been said and written about the health hazards from dog faeces, I am convinced that the aesthetic unpleasantness is probably more important.

Unfortunately most of us who are dog owners are embarrassed when our dogs defecate in the middle of a pavement and quickly walk away, leaving someone else to tread in it. In the urban or suburban situation in which most dogs are kept today, this short-sighted attitude can only lead to more restrictive legislation. We just have to face up to the responsibilities of dog ownership. What goes in must come out! We feed our dogs and they are going to defecate and at times, no matter how well trained, they are going to make mistakes. Being embarrassed about them is not going to help. In the Netherlands and some other Continental countries there is a positive attitude in that many local authorities provide litter bins into which dog faeces have to be placed, on payment of a fine for defaulters. The carrying of a polythene bag in the pocket is a hygenic method of overcoming the dog's mistakes, for the faeces can be grasped through the polythene, which can then be turned inside out with the faeces inside, knotted and quietly dropped into the nearest litter receptacle. Some manufacturers actually make specially constructed bags with a rigid opening with which the faeces can be grasped and then turned inside out over the contents.

Unfortunately, due to the common, almost subconscious embarrassment on the part of owners, the idea has just not caught on in this country. It seems to me that until there is a co-ordinated effort on the part of the dog owning public to accept that these tasks are part of their responsibility we can only expect to be faced with increasingly restrictive legislation.

However much we admire the stand taken by those

public spirited individuals who, despite the responsibilities of families and pets, are prepared to go to jail rather than stop walking their dogs in local parks, I personally feel that they could probably achieve far more if they spent their time campaigning among dog owners to take a more responsible and less embarrassed attitude towards their pets' waste products. It is no use trying to ignore what will occur as naturally as night follows day and leave it for somebody else to walk in. If it occurs in a place that could cause annoyance, clearing it up at the time it is voided removes from those members of the community who do not quite view the foibles of our pets in the same light as we do their main cause for complaint. Then the activities of the anti-dog lobby will not cause any trepidation to any member of the dog owning public, no matter where they live.

Index